Edinburgh Review

EDITOR: Brian McCabe

ASSISTANT EDITOR & PRODUCTION: Jennie Renton

Website Development: Peter Likarish

22a Buccleuch Place
Edinburgh EH8 9LN

edinburgh.review@ed.ac.uk
www.edinburghreview.org.uk

EDITORIAL BOARD: Cairns Craig, Kimberly Hutchings, A.L. Kennedy,
Andrew O'Hagan

ADVISORY BOARD: Karina Dent, Gavin Miller, Benjamin Morris,
David Moses

ISSN 0267 6672

Edinburgh Review 118 ISBN 1 85933 227 7

Printed and bound in the UK by the Cromwell Press Ltd,
Trowbridge, Wiltshire.

Supported by

Scottish
Arts Council

Subscribe to *Edinburgh Review*

Individual subscriptions (3 issues annually) £17 / $27 / 27 Euros
Institutional subscriptions (3 issues annually) £34 / $54 / 54 Euros

Please complete and return this subscription form to *Edinburgh Review*,
22a Buccleuch Place, Edinburgh, EH8 9LN.

BACK ISSUES are available at £5. Please contact our office for availability
information or to place an order.

Subscription Form

Name:

Address:

Postcode:

I wish to subscribe to *Edinburgh Review*, beginning from issue _____.
I enclose payment for £17 (individual) / £34 (institutional)*
[* = delete as applicable]

Please make cheques payable to '*Edinburgh Review*'

To pay by Credit / Debit Card, please complete details below:

Type of Card: VISA / Mastercard / Switch [delete as appropriate]

Card Number : _____ _____ _____ _____

Card Valid from : __ / __ / __ to : __ / __ / __ Issue No : __ [Switch only]

Signature : _____ Date : __ / __ / __

Contents

Editorial

This issue looks to Africa, presenting work by renowned writers such as Jack Mapanje and Fred D'Aguiar, but also showcasing work by both mentors and participants from an extraordinary educational project, 'Crossing Borders', funded by the British Council and administered by Lancaster University. The project was the brainchild of Graham Mort, and in his essay he sets out the project's genesis and development and goes beyond that to consider writing in Africa in a broader sense.

I took part in this project as a mentor myself, working with emergent writers from various African countries such as Cameroon, Malawi, Uganda, Zambia and Zimbabwe. The work was always refreshing and sometimes it struck me as very different from current fiction and poetry in the UK. In terms of subject alone, much of the work was dealing with such things as tribal warfare, civil war, political corruption, poverty, AIDS, genocide. Much of it had a keen political edge, and satire played an important part, as in Gabriel Gidi's very Swiftian piece, 'Dear Honourable Member'.

This issue also presents articles on African cinema and the Scotland-Malawi Partnership, and G.P. Kennedy's 'Let There Be Light' documents one Scottish woman's extraordinary quest for truth in Rwanda after the genocide there.

Brian McCabe, Editor

Acknowledgements

'Double Shame' by Beatrice Fri Bime is from her second collection of short stories, *Someplace, Somewhere*, Patron Publishing House, Cameroon: 2005.

'Mapungubwe' by Henning Pieterse is from *Die Burg van Hertog Bloubaard* (*Duke Bluebeard's Castle*), translated from Afrikaans by Henning and Hetta Pieterse. Tafelberg, Cape Town: 2000.

Thanks to British Museum Publishing and Rebecca Jewell for permission to reproduce three images from *African Designs* by Rebecca Jewell: 'Asante calabash bowls from Ghana with very fine engraved patterns of flowers and animals.'

Part I

Crossing Borders

Crossing Borders

Graham Mort

In 2001, when working as a freelance writer in education, I was asked by the British Council to take up a six-week writing residency at the University of Makerere in Uganda. The Crossing Borders project was conceived during that residency in response to the problems that emerging writers in that country were facing: lack of literature infrastructure, lack of publishing opportunities, a fossilised 'English' literature curriculum and lack of educational or workshop experience in relation to writing development. I've written elsewhere about the detailed educational strategy behind this distance learning project and its use of information technology to link writers in the UK to those in Africa. Accounts of this process can be found on the Crossing Borders website: www. crossingborders-africanwriting.org.

In 2003, a small-scale pilot project expanded to include nine participating countries: Uganda, Malawi, Nigeria, Ghana, Zambia, South Africa, Zimbabwe, Cameroon and Kenya. The project continued to be funded by the British Council, but was now managed from the department of English and Creative Writing at Lancaster University, where I had become director of its postgraduate writing programme. We recruited Tara Duce as project manager and brought in the writer and distance learning expert, Sara Maitland, to organise our network of mentors. Hannah Henderson in London coordinated and led British Council support. Over the next three years, more than

200 African writers entered the programme to be mentored by a group of twenty-five professional writers in the UK – all drawn from diverse cultural and intercultural backgrounds. Without the expertise and loyalty of the management team and the dedicated acts of support and interpretation that were carried out by mentors, the project would have remained a paper exercise. Instead, they gave it shape, life and variation within its necessarily tight logistical framework.

All tutorial exchange was achieved by email and attachment files. The British Council offices across Africa acted as electronic post boxes, but other IT outlets were also used. Sometimes writers brought handwritten drafts of their work to Internet cafes in Nairobi, Kampala, Lagos or Lilongwe, re-drafting their work in sweltering heat as the traffic crawled by outside. Despite infrastructural difficulties, we had one huge advantage: exchange of text in electronic form is particularly suited to the collaborative development of new writing. The emerging text remains ductile and a mentor is easily able to intervene, using 'track changes', inserting comments, or actually redrafting sections of the work to 'show not tell' when making a point.

Writing development and cultural knowledge flowed in both directions and nearly all of our mentors were able to make a visit to Africa to run live workshops. In October 2005 I worked with the Council to develop Beyond Borders, an international festival and conference of Creative Writing that brought together delegates from seventeen Anglophone African countries and eight writers from the UK. As well as staging celebratory events and readings, the festival incorporated a series of carefully constructed public discussions underpinned by key research questions. A rapporteur was assigned to each forum and the resulting reports have been edited and collated into a consultative document that will help to shape literature development strategies in Africa for the future, based on the desires, hopes and needs of African writers.

The Council had asked me to take up the residency at Makerere in 2001 on an exploratory basis and it proved to be a remarkable learning curve. My visit was delayed because of violence on the campus and when I eventually made the flight, the country was in the grip of a general election. President Museveni, hero of the bush war against Milton Obote, was seeking a third term of office. The campus at Makerere was eerily quiet since it was half term and most staff and students had gone home to their villages to vote. There were bombs in downtown Kampala, large-scale killings in Kasesi and Murchison Falls, and rumours of a civil war if Museveni prevailed against his former ally, Dr. Colonel Kizzi Besige. Ugandan troops were being recalled from the Congo and drove chanting through Kampala in open-topped trucks.

A show of strength. There were more killings at the university and a student demonstration against them was put down by soldiers with automatic weapons and tear gas. I stayed at the guest house on Makerere campus and breakfasted to CNN news. That winter it brought images of foot and mouth disease in the UK, burning pyres of cows and sheep. Before I left North Yorkshire I'd walked out to see the first lambs playing in the fields: now fire and slaughter were desolating the landscape.

I kept an extensive diary of that first visit. I've since made many more, traversing the continent, but my attitude to Africa as a writer has only deepened in its ambivalence. The more I understood, the less able I was to write about it. As a writer from a working class background in the Lancashire cotton belt, I felt expiated from any post-colonial guilt. Yet many of the mills in my hometown carried the names of African countries, regions, or colonial rulers. My own great uncle, a joiner from Preston, had become a Methodist missionary in the Belgian Congo before being killed by rebels in 1961. The irony of Asian and Afro-Caribbean mill workers migrating to Lancashire to share its post-industrial decline was tangible: both indigenous and incoming workers felt the effects as the hulks of mills loomed to haunt those Pennine towns. My grandfather had been a mule spinner and my own roots were, unwittingly, deep in Empire. My father was a piano technician and the piano itself has come to symbolise the colonial enterprise for me: ebony, ivory, copper and mahogany from Africa, steel from Sheffield, felt from Yorkshire. The musical repertoire of the piano itself represented the apogee of European musical culture with its harmonic complexity and sophistication – all accommodated in that polished cabinet into which God knows how much human suffering had gone.

Those thoughts were almost subterranean during my first visits to Africa, a growing disquiet, a sense of belonging and dislocation. That sense of familiarity was the strangest feeling. On my first flight to Uganda, the plane stopped over at Nairobi early in the morning. Beyond a horizon of flat-topped trees seeped a thin line of blood – my first African dawn. Screaming above the runway were migrating swifts, the same birds that nested in my village in North Yorkshire: a connection with Africa that was ancient and primal in its seasonal rhythm. Then flying over Lake Victoria to touch down in Uganda, with its extraordinarily vivid landscape, wildlife and people: red-dirt roads, bicycles carrying impossible loads of charcoal and sugar-cane, wandering Ancholi cattle and goats, mopeds ridden by three adults with a baby balanced on the handlebars, women bearing baskets of plantain or yellow jerry-cans of water on their heads, a blazing sky full of kites, vultures and marabou

11

storks, billowing thunderheads each afternoon and dramatic tropical storms at night. At dusk the atmosphere was choked with diesel fumes and sickly, rotting vegetation. Then thousands of fruit bats flying from the trees. Then grasshopper choirs of sudden, equatorial dark.

Add to that the vestiges of British Empire: Ugandan children in 1950s school uniforms, the university buildings built like my old grammar school in Oldham, the prevalent and quaintly elegant use of English. All this underlain with a bloody recent history that belied the gentle good humour and impeccable manners of the Ugandans I met each day. It was bewildering and beguiling. I was drawn back again and again, but always the outsider, the muzungu. At times poverty and human degradation were overwhelming. It's hard to look at amputation, AIDS, hunger, leprosy, polio; one day I bent down to put some coins into a woman's hand and found she had no fingers. I came to wear the European's badge of shame – my thousand-yard stare.

In Africa, I have the privilege to work with the most committed writers I've ever met. Writers struggling, not with existential anxieties, but the immediacies of war, disease and premature death in many forms. Added to political and biological determinants are lack of education, economic opportunity, and civil rights. Yet here are writers who believe that their work can bear witness, can even change the political and social conditions under which they live. In short, they believe that literature might negotiate better terms for the human condition. It's exhilarating, moving and – given the huge problems with literature infrastructure in most African countries – an enterprise that is almost always committed to failure.

Crossing Borders has led to significant actual exchange between Africa and the UK and a number of African writers have taken up writing residencies here through the project. Our website now publishes a regular magazine of new African writing. A few weeks ago, when speaking at the British Council Oxford Conference, I met an Argentinian teacher who was pulling new writing from the Crossing Borders website to work with her students on another continent, citing it as the most accessible source of contemporary African literature. I'm currently designing a new British Council project to work through radio and the production of print-on-demand books in Uganda. We hope that pilot has the potential to mature into a much bigger project, spanning orature and literature, English and indigenous languages.

We await the positive effects of the Commission for Africa and the G8 summit of 2005 that recommended a whole range of developments from trade reform to support for cultural industries and enterprise. Meanwhile, a new interest in Africa has developed, which, in some ways, is an uneasy reiteration of the power of western countries to exploit its history and resources. Films such as *The Interpreter, The Constant Gardener*, and *Shooting Dogs* often hide a Eurocentric viewpoint – that is rarely critiqued – behind worthy thematic material. The moral seems to be a sentimentalised one: Africa must be saved by Europeans since its own people are either incompetent, indistinguishably numerous, savage or corrupt. Such messages need to be vigorously rejected in recognition of the extraordinary cultural contribution that Africa has made to the developed world. Crossing Borders showed the huge benefits to UK artists in engaging with Africa. The challenge is to work together to develop strategies appropriate to conditions there and to enable new cultural and economic production.

My own writing continues to inhabit an ambivalent and troubled space in relation to Africa. Yet creative writing is an attempt at understanding. Despite cultural and linguistic differences, fundamental sympathies of human experience link us together. The journeys I've made to Africa have changed my life, challenging its integrity and saturating my imagination. Behind a door in the corridor of the English Department at Lancaster University is a modest office with a map of Africa and a computer seething with intercontinental communication. Our enterprise has gradually begun to link to other research at the University. I'm now involved in a major AHRC-funded project, Moving Manchester: Mediating Marginalities relating to writings of migration and diaspora in Greater Manchester. With other colleagues, I'm developing a web platform – Trans-Scriptions – that will link together an array of seminar and research activity relating to writing culture and location. Distance learning methodology informs our teaching through new hybrid virtual/actual environments and our postgraduates increasingly resemble an intercultural community of writers, with PhD students from Welsh, Pakistani, Indian, Caribbean and African backgrounds. New British Academy funding for UK/ Africa links offers the possibility of extending this to an international writing community through collaboration with overseas partners.

Literature has always inhabited the virtual domain of the human imagination. It combines seamlessly with electronic virtuality that can be linked to e-learning, podcasting, digital broadcasting, wind-up and solar powered receivers. Cutting-edge technologies can be linked to pragmatic ones that really work in the developing world. By 2007 we hope to make this vision a reality that can be accessed by African writers and the growing audience for African writing worldwide. I believe this emergent literature can influence economic, social and cultural changes; I'm optimistic that those, in turn, can bear the hopes, visions and aspirations of its authors.

Zimbabwe Through Its Writers

Martin Goodman

'Writing matters in Zimbabwe.' The statement comes from the Harare publisher Irene Staunton. It's a truth for publishers in Zimbabwe, like 'etiquette matters in the ring' is a truth for prize boxers. They touch gloves, bow, then prepare to get the hell beaten out of them. How do you bring out books when people are poor and inflation is touching 1,000 per cent? Where's the commercial logic in such a thing? Who needs novels in any case, aren't they just escapist? Irene Staunton gives her working life as her response:

> For me, fiction is more important than history. Some truths can only be told through fiction. We can never understand wars, conflicts, love, and how things go wrong without fiction. We can never get inside the complexities and understand how small mistakes can turn into terrible issues. The best history of Zimbabwe's liberation war has been told through fiction, told as complex and compelling story, as seen from all sides with no one perspective.

A buzz was going around Harare in January. Tsitsi Dangarembga wrote one splendid debut novel, *Nervous Conditions*, then declared she was abandoning fiction for film. Now the rumours said she was writing again. *Nervous Conditions* led the girl Tamba from village life into a mission school education, a great fracturing of culture that had sadly damaged the lives of her cousins. Tamba's duty was to use her education, her reading, to render that fracturing whole again within herself. The mending is both the mending of a writer, and the mending that can be affected by a writer. Final words of the book declare, 'Quietly, unobtrusively and extremely fitfully, something in my mind began to assert itself, to question things and refuse to be brainwashed, bringing me to this time when I can set down this story.'

'Tsitsi Dangarembga has a very supportive husband,' the writer Virginia Phiri told me. 'Men don't want women to have more about them. One woman writer's husband used her manuscript for his roll-ups and smoked it.'

Phiri has a supportive husband. She paid for publication of her novel *Desperate* herself. The book was an act of homage to the sex workers who had sheltered her during her own fighting days in the liberation war. Without their protection and food she would have died. The book is filled with the fictionalised tales of these women. It shows the circumstances that led them to prostitution, the sad run of disaster, abandonment and oppression that leads them to make 'desperate' choices; it also has the strength to go off-message and explore the women's sexuality. Writers teaching in Bulawayo have installed the book on the curriculum for trainee teachers, inspired by its daring and the power of its telling. 'Are you still African?' people have asked of Phiri, as though crossing social boundaries means leaving your nationhood behind. 'Africa is an oral culture,' she explains in response. 'The orality of things is selective – we choose what we talk about. Self-censorship in an author is very serious. I don't intend to annoy anyone. When most writers stop self-censoring, we will bring out what we want to say.'

Fountain pen in hand, the writer Charles Mungoshi recently spent a month as 'writer in residence' at Irene Staunton's Weaver Press. Painstakingly the words and the sentences built up into an exquisite story of five pages, 'Chizuva', in the collection of stories by new and established writers, *Writing Now*. Mungoshi's novel *Waiting for the Rain* should have had the Nobel Prize Committee sitting to attention when it came out in 1975, when Mungoshi was just twenty-seven. In that novel the boy Lucifer has won an art scholarship which will take him from his Zimbabwean village to city life in England. The novel is the tale of Lucifer's departure.

Lucifer has an older brother, the itinerant musician and drummer Garabha. Garabha holds dear what Lucifer despises, cares for his family and honours his traditions, yet his father disowns him in favour of the younger, departing Lucifer. The book does speak of a new world order coming to destroy and devalue the old, yet beyond that it tells the value of art.

While Lucifer's departure is trumpeted, Garabha leaves the village in secret, because he knows he will cry, unable 'to stop the foreboding feeling that his brother is chasing the wind'. As he walks away, his grandfather hears a song leave with him, fading into the bush:

It is only later that he realises that the song and the tune are not any of the old war chants. It must be something that the boy has made up himself, he concludes. Made up with the unerring ear of the old musicians. With a heart that can make such poetry, the Old Man feels, the boy is Home, the house is in order. But the boy doesn't know it yet. He is still searching. Good for him. It means he will find what he is looking for… he isn't far away now.

The book is taut with family conflict, with character, with tenderness and longing, with issues drawn from primal social conflict and change. Yet quietly, it is a work of art in praise of the artist. Not the artist Lucifer who manufactures a style to appeal to others, but the truth of Garabha who tells essential tales with his drum. "And he says he hasn't got a thing to give anybody – the foolishness of youth." The Old Man chuckles to himself and attacks his work with renewed zest.'

'A young writer came up to me and said "I loved your *Waiting for the Rain*", the novelist Shimmer Chinodya told me. 'I say go away and don't come back till you know what books I've written.' His first novel, *Dew in the Morning*, was written when he was eighteen.

I grew up in the countryside in the Sixties and Seventies. That first book is about the land question, Smith shunting blacks into bad areas. The land question was before Zanu PF – this country's steeped in land issues. Do you wait fifty years to start on the land situation, or do you just start and then fix the problems as you go? Why was the war fought? What does the average Zimbabwean have? Go into the rural areas and you meet real poverty – no trees or schools or clinics and the rivers are silted. It is the writer's obligation to write about what is happening. How do you say it intelligently, convincingly and creatively? We need intelligence. Do that extra something to rise above the common voice.

Shimmer Chinodya and I were meeting over beers in a Harare café. His new novel *Chairman of Fools* was the city's must-read book. An earlier novel, *Farai's Girls,* was frankly autobiographical. Farai reappears in this book, a writer in Harare seeking to repair his fractured life. Bipolar disorder results in a breakdown, seeing Farai elected 'Chairman of Fools' among the inmates of an asylum. Both in the breakdown of a writer's life, and its painful and gradual reassembly, the book is a powerful primer for anyone seeking insights into Zimbabwe's writing life in.

Chinodya waves his hands in the air in mock confession to the autobiographical nature of this work:

Four or five other colleagues have gone through the same experience of bipolar disorder. In Zimbabwe there is the added pressure of fending for one's family. In the eyes of the public writers are up against lawyers and accountants. That pressure can destroy us. Most people are young and go-getters – the question is, how do you paddle your own canoe?

An award took him on a writer's residency to Italy, another aspect of his life fictionalised as a feature of this new novel.

When I went to Italy I took my book in my head with me. I wrote *Chairman of Fools* there in five weeks. It was a convenience. But I must think my book out here and talk to people. Things change so quickly in Zimbabwe you can't stay out too long. Four to six years is not right.

Some people still ask, 'When are you going to get a proper job?' I've written forty-nine books – [seven literary the other text books.] Language text books – I used to be ashamed of them but I'm not any more. I'm very, very proud of what I do in Zimbabwe. I write creative books that are exciting and interesting for children. Writing is a profession. We take ourselves damn seriously.

Chinodya's classic novel is *Harvest of Thorns*, written in self-imposed exile as an MA thesis at Iowa. 'In the US all writers were minimalists. I learnt to clip my style, to be more precise and simple.' The novel:

was about thirty to forty years of Zimbabwean life. One third of Benjamin in that book is me. His school and urban life is my life. What happens to a thirteen or fourteen-year-old when he's thrown into the thick of war while pubescing? What does it do to his relationships? It's a psychological examination of war on young people. War is inevitable in most Zimbabwean writing. It's so much a part of our psyche.

African writing is good for the English language. It is totally African though Anglophone. Language is a way of life and expression and identity. At school we spelled very well, though we mispronounced the words. My writing is an act of revenge – all that grammar they shoved down my throat, I'm going to use it and create something totally hybrid. It is well written but the voice must shock you. My use of English must show the complexity of the African thought processes. Most books haven't tackled the complexity of the African mind. Ultimately that's why my books all sound so different. I'm searching for the complexity of options and choices and values. I'm trying to salvage the African mind from decades of abuse and misconception.

I'm a funny mix. I look confident. All serious writers are not sure of themselves. Writing is a process of self discovery. You can't sit down and write a book and know what you're doing. Afterwards you can say 'I didn't know that much about myself'. Writing is modesty.

There is so much resilience here. Perhaps that's not been acknowledged. A West African country might have had ten coups by now. We are maybe too tolerant. The western press is deliberate in their viciousness. You need to live here to know what is happening. The foreign press exaggerates the situation in Zimbabwe. Read *The Standard* for an example of a free newspaper. They have wicked cartoons of Mugabe for example. Some papers have been shut down but nobody has been killed or locked up. Writers haven't been subtle enough to challenge the government. We have to challenge the system in a very subtle way, not just offer the clichés the west expects to hear.

I write about the psychology of being a writer – being a writer in Zimbabwe. I'm a colonial victim. They forced me to speak in English. I talked, dreamt, laughed in English, went to the toilet in English. I'm not good enough in Shona. English is enriching. I draw from two cultures. I draw from my Shona experience and educated English.

Family ritual is the other side of the African mind. Going to church on a Sunday morning and a jazz show in the afternoon. In the west it's each man for himself. Africanness is not necessarily material. It's a sense of family, of some values, of spiritualism. If I took you to an African wedding or a kitchen party you would know what I mean. It's the paying of *Lobola*, the bride price. Some things have to be done properly. Maybe we are losing things with TV, video, DVDs, etc. Things must change, but if we lose our Africanness we lose ourselves. We must be able to compromise.

Ignatius Mabasa is at the forefront of writing in Shona, the majority language of Zimbabwe. His novel *Mapenzi* was voted one of the top seventy-five Zimbabwean books of the century. A current project is to translate Dangarembga's *Nervous Conditions* into Shona. He sees three tiers of writers in the country:

The first generation of writers were products of colonial education. Mostly teachers or priests, their writing was didactic, delivering a moral message. The next generation started by glorifying the revolutionary war, and moved on to questioning it and their own identity. Zimbabwe has a new generation of writers, the 'born frees', who did not experience the war. Born in the city, they do not have that transition from country to city to deal with. There is a hunger to hear them, but there is a drought in publishing. Publishers bring out either no books, or one or two novels a year. Manuscripts are returned unread. The born-frees are not being heard.

But they are writing. Born-frees and their elders brought a fresh demand to my workshops in Harare and Bulawayo. They wanted to learn how to lead their own workshops, to carry the vigour and freedom of artistic expression into community groups and schools. What is writing? It's something you can spin out of your private world then dare to share. It's letting yourself be vulnerable when it makes much more practical sense to shield yourself. It's daring to imagine your way into the whole spectrum of being human. A workshop exercise brought group poems out of Harare and Bulawayo, students writing individual lines then gathering to select, discard and arrange them till they had poems that spoke some sort of joint truth. Here are two of their poems.

What is writing in Harare?
It is the assurance
something is
going on in my head,
engrossing, captivating
– revisiting my mind

It takes me many places,
Makes me many people
– expressing thoughts, experiences.
It ties everything together,
like dreaming.

And what does writing mean in Bulawayo?
It is an exploration of my nakedness
Livening and beautifying my being
Cleansing my emotions
A therapy that brings healing

It is a weapon, sharp and incisive
Challenging taboos and boundaries
A deep well of teachings, thoughts and activities
A fulfilling experience.

Let There Be Light

G.P. Kennedy

Rwanda is a small landlocked country in the Great Lakes region of central Africa, a verdant land of hills and lush countryside, lying a few degrees south of the equator. In 1994 its population was approximately eight million, divided between two ethnic groups, Hutus (84 per cent) and Tutsis (16 per cent).

Between April and June 1994, an estimated 800,000 Rwandans were killed in the space of 100 days. Most of those killed were Tutsis – and most of those killing were Hutus: this was not 'collateral damage' inflicted by 'smart bombs', this was mass slaughter by machetes shipped in under the guise of 'agricultural tools' and given to Hutus for the hacking.

The genocide was sparked by the death of the then Rwandan president, Juvenal Habyarimana, a Hutu, when his plane was shot down above the country's capital, Kigali, on 6 April 1994. It was widely held that the rebel RPF, a Tutsi group in exile for many years in bordering Uganda and Zaire (now Democratic Republic of Congo), was responsible for the rocket attack.

There have always been ethnic tension between the Hutus and Tutsis, but this animosity was exacerbated during Belgian colonial rule and has not abated since its end in 1962.

Into this ethno-political context stepped Lesley Bilinda, a Scottish nurse working for Tearfund, an 'Evangelical Christian relief and development charity working in partnership to bring help and hope to communities in need around the world'.

In October 1989 Bilinda was returning to head up a nursing outreach program, based in the town of Gahini, in the east of Rwanda, having enjoyed a voluntary placement at Gahini Hospital in 1987. Living with a local family, learning the language – Kinyarwandan – and becoming a valuable part of the community, Bilinda grew to love Rwanda and Rwandans in short order, with their ever-open arms, and doors. She fell in love, marrying local English teacher Charles Bilinda in 1992 – a time when the menace of sporadic attacks on civilians across Rwanda was beginning to grow.

The appalling experiences that were to follow for Rwanda, and Bilinda's very personal experience of the genocide, its aftermath, and the search for truth and the hope of subsequent reconciliation with the past, form the basis for two books, *The Colour of Darkness: A Personal Story of Tragedy and Hope in Rwanda* (Hodder and Stoughton, 1996) and *With What Remains: A Widow's Quest for Truth in Rwanda* (Hodder and Stoughton, 2006), and a documentary film, *Hunting My Husband's Killers* (Grace Productions and Purple Flame Media, 2005).

I do not intend to take up printed space with a lengthy critique of the works; it is inappropriate to the recounting of deeply personal experiences published due to genuine widespread public interest and a desire and need on Bilinda's part to share her story with others, that it might provide a platform for Rwandan issues and succour for those who have suffered loss, both in Rwanda and more broadly.

For me, the central issue in respect of Bilinda's works is that of the nature of faith, Christian faith to be more exact; how it is exercised in circumstances as dire as those Lesley Bilinda has found herself in since 1994. It does, therefore, behove me to outline the core people and events involved with the work.

The first chapters of *The Colour of Darkness* portray the challenges and delights of living in the home of Bilinda's Rwandan hosts, Etienne and Emeralde, with their five children and the persistent stream of guests whom they entertained each day, at all hours; the staple diet of beans and very little meat; the trips to the long drop (toilet) across a boggy patch, in wellingtons two sizes too small; the language barrier, broken down rapidly by Bilinda with a mix of assiduousness and saturation.

These people, places and events are followed by an outline of her relationship with Charles Bilinda. She gives insight into their time together, their burgeoning love and their search for divine guidance as to how best to advance their relationship. Bilinda alludes to types and degrees of opposition and challenges to their inter-racial, cross-cultural marriage.

Having worked tirelessly with Charles to establish a home and professional life together, Bilinda receives her sister from Scotland, days before the death of President Habyarimana, and takes off to Kenya for a holiday. Charles refuses to accompany them, considering a trip abroad 'inappropriate' at that time.

The genocidal conflict that follows is delivered with a stark chronological and statistical clarity that makes it all the more chilling, though Bilinda is at all times mired in the deeply personal aspect, trapped in Kenya unable to receive word of Charles and refused passage into Rwanda. Bilinda not only describes her personal struggle but also includes testimonies from her Rwandan friends, family and colleagues of courage, fear and sorrow.

With Rwanda a 'no-go' zone, and feeling helpless and beyond exhaustion in the heat of Nairobi, Bilinda is forced to return to Scotland in April 1994, to begin the 'long, long wait in darkness'. Here she attempts to resurrect an old life, as she becomes resigned to Charles' murder. It is safe to return to Rwanda in September 1994. She discovers the miracle that all of her husband's family has survived... with one notable exception. It then becomes apparent that Charles was killed in Butare, southwestern Rwanda, while there on diocesan work. After trips to Butare and the vast Tanzanian refugee camp at Benaco, Bilinda leaves the reader as she makes an attempt at 'Picking up the Pieces' in the final chapter.

For a decade Lesley Bilinda lived with no knowledge of how Charles died, or the identity of his killers. She returned to Rwanda in 2004, with a documentary film crew to attempt to uncover the truth. *With What Remains* tells the tale of this trip, during which Bilinda confronts the men she suspected were responsible for her husband's death. An unexpected truth emerged: that Charles Bilinda had been having an affair before and during their marriage.

The beautifully written and genuinely affecting story charts Bilinda's physical and emotional journey through a post-genocide Rwanda still shrouded in deceit and confusion. The pathetic fallacy herein is powerful, the socio-political climate of Rwanda mirroring Bilinda's emotional and psychological quest for clarity. Despite the painful revelations, she gains a new sense of freedom from knowing the truth, and a fresh belief in herself and in God. Gavin Cargill, cameraman on the same trip, filming for the documentary *Hunting My Husband's Killers,* declared of the book, 'It is not only an accurate account of the trip, but a window into a world which many of us will never encounter and a brutally honest assessment of the hard choices and emotional reactions made in the face of the worst atrocities of the last decade.'

Lesley Bilinda's story is intensely personal yet objective and original, enormously painful yet filled with compassion. The key message of the book is one of emancipation, through the ability to confront overcome immense trauma and 'make music with what remains'; and through forgiveness, as 'forgiveness addresses the imbalance of power' (between victim and perpetrator).

Hunting My Husband's Killers is a visual documentary of the trip undertaken in *With What Remains*. Bilinda's search begins at the guesthouse where Charles was last seen. Its then manager, Pastor Kabarira, believed to have colluded with Hutu rebels, is now in prison. He claims to have watched Charles being taken away by a man in military uniform. Bilinda confronts him in Butare Prison but he refuses to admit guilt, stating, 'If I had colluded with the militias, I would admit to it and ask for forgiveness.'

Upon her return to Gahini, Bilinda learns of a local man, Gasto, who is prepared to speak about the killings. But as they talk, it becomes clear that Gasto was one of the men who murdered her best friend, Anatolie. 'We sliced her neck. She died instantly,' Gasto confesses. They also attacked Anatolie's young child with a machete. 'Part of me felt disgust that he should be there and involved with it but part of me also felt, I suppose, pity for him. I offered him forgiveness. It meant a lot to him, and lifted a burden for me,' Bilinda reports quite remarkably.

Bilinda met a number of women who confirmed her late husband had been having an affair. In spite of this, she gained from her trip, finding herself able to 'let go of what they [the killers] may have done in order to free myself from the burden of resentment and anger. But I don't know that there will ever be closure.'

How on earth Lesley Bilinda was able to accept the killings of her perfidious husband, her closest friends, colleagues and in excess of 800,000 of her adopted countrymen and women yet retain her faith in God is perhaps a question for another time. That through her faith, absolute, blind or otherwise, Lesley Bilinda is bringing hope and charity to a devastated nation of the most tumultuous continent is a fact that nobody should ignore.

'No One Can Shave Your Head in Your Absence'

Scotland and Malawi Today

Kenneth R. Ross

Introduction: the Livingstone Legacy

Links between Scotland and Malawi (formerly Nyasaland) began with David Livingstone's journeys up the Zambezi and Shire rivers to Lake Malawi in 1859.[1] Not only his life of friendship and engagement with the 'Nyasa' people but, even more, his death in central Africa galvanised the people of Scotland to make a commitment to this particular region, long before the borders of the modern nation of Malawi had been set. In the mid-1870s both the Church of Scotland and the Free Church of Scotland established missions, the former in the south, the latter in the north and before long, a two-way movement of people and ideas was under way.[2] Placing emphasis on education and healthcare, the churches worked alongside the African Lakes Company, embodying Livingstone's vision of Christianity and commerce as the solution to the evil of the slave trade in Africa.[3]

When, in the late 1880s, it seemed that southern Malawi might become part of Portuguese East Africa, a popular campaign in Scotland and a heavily subscribed public petition persuaded the British Government that this must not be allowed to happen, and Nyasaland came into being as a British Protectorate.[4] Likewise, when Cecil Rhodes was eager to incorporate

Nyasaland in his British South Africa Company, it was the Scottish missions which frustrated his ambitions and secured Nyasaland's Protectorate status.[5]

In 1961 historian George Shepperson observed that the Scots' pioneering of British Central Africa and their spirited opposition to its passing to Portugal may be envisaged as the attempt by a group of peoples who had all the aspirations of a nation, but little of the structure and substance of one, to make a final fling at acquiring the Caledonian colony which had been denied them since the failure of the seventeenth-century Darien venture.[6] In the 1950s, when Nyasaland did fall into the clutches of the racist Federation of Rhodesia and Nyasaland, its predicament was debated in the Church of Scotland General Assembly, which did much to persuade the British Government that independence was the proper path for Malawi.[7] And in the early 1990s, when Malawians struggled to break free from a decadent one-party system, the Church of Scotland was again a significant source of support.[8]

The 'come and go' between Scotland and Malawi has touched the experience of many families and communities in both nations. In the military, the civil service, the legal profession, engineering, agriculture, religion, education, healthcare, commerce – in almost every sector of national life there is a history of shared engagement. Less tangible, but no less significant, are the personal influences. There are Scots whose lives have been enriched by the opportunity to share in the love and the laughter of community life in Malawi. There are Malawians who have discovered that the apparently dour Scots can be the most loyal of friends. Shepperson highlights the affinity between the two nations:

> The predominant European culture in Nyasaland until very recent times has been Scottish: in fact, the histories of Scotland and Nyasaland pursue remarkably parallel courses. Both are poor; but both have distinctive educational traditions which have reinforced the conviction of their many migrants that they are worth better jobs than their homeland can offer them. From such conditions, there has sprung up in both countries a very definite radicalism, at home and abroad.[9]

Partnership Rekindled

The close relationship between the two nations, which continued uninterrupted following Malawi's independence in 1964, was given a fresh momentum six years ago, when the Malawi Millennium Project was launched by Strathclyde University, which incorporates David Livingstone's alma mater, and Bell College, the higher education institution closest to his birthplace. As well as catching the imagination of a new generation of Scots, it has completed significant development projects in Malawi.[10] The fresh enthusiasm gave rise in 2004 to the Scotland-Malawi Partnership, a civil society alliance whose objective is to 'reduce and relieve poverty in Malawi, particularly, but not exclusively, by targeting the health and education sectors'.[11] A Malawi Board has also been formed to build up the Malawi end of the partnership.

This rekindling of Scotland's relationship with Malawi has coincided with the creation of the Scottish Parliament. Although foreign affairs is a 'reserved power' at Westminster, the Scottish First Minister, Jack McConnell made an official visit to Malawi in May 2005 and the following November there was a return visit by President Bingu wa Mutharika on the occasion of the Scotland-Malawi Conference. The Cooperation Agreement between the Scottish Executive and the Malawi Government states:

> Scotland and Malawi have a long history of collaboration, particularly in health and education. Both countries share a wish to build upon this history by actively engaging through partnership. This is a reciprocal partnership based upon sharing experiences and skills. It is an opportunity to learn from each other and to recognise the needs of our two countries.[12]

It identifies civic governance and society, sustainable economic development, health and education as broad themes on which collaboration will be developed. The Executive's International Development Fund is supporting initiatives in these areas, with £2.4 million being granted in 2005.[13] That same year, a Scottish Parliament Cross-Party Group on Malawi was established, with the aim to:

> develop and enhance links between Scotland and Malawi and to provide a forum for discussion on these matters. In particular the group will focus on links between the two parliaments and between civil society in each country. In order to achieve this, the group will work with parliamentarians from each legislature, with Malawians living in Scotland and with other organisations working in Malawi.[14]

This agenda was taken forward by the visit of a Scottish Parliamentary delegation, including representations from all parties, to Malawi in February 2006. The Malawi connection found exuberant expression within the Parliament in June 2006 when the songs of the Limbe CCAP Choir echoed around the Garden Lobby, demonstrating one particular level at which Malawi has great riches to share with Scotland.

The Scotland-Malawi relationship is finding expression in many different ways. The Government to Government relationship draws its vitality from the multitude of links made by civil society – schools, universities, health boards, local government, faith-based organisations, etc. There is consciousness of the need for the partnership to be genuinely two-sided. Memories in Malawi are long enough to recall the colonialist idea of partnership, described by Lord Malvern as the partnership between the rider and the horse.[15] A very different aspiration was evident at the Scotland-Malawi Partnership Conference.[16] The inadequacies of a donor-recipient model of international development were trenchantly exposed and the value of a relationship grounded in mutual respect and a commitment to learn from each other was affirmed and celebrated.

'A Very Definite Radicalism'

A primary obstacle to a two-way partnership is the extent of the disparity in resources between the two partners. The per capita GDP in Malawi is US$605 while in Scotland it is US$27,147.[17] In other words, the average Scot is 45 times better off than the average Malawian. No wonder that Scots visiting Malawi are struck by the shocking level of poverty which blights people's lives and determined to take action to alleviate it. This positive commitment has motivated much of the current renewal in Scotland-Malawi relations. No one could question its good intentions but it can easily be undermined by two sets of dynamics. The first is that the relationship of the two countries comes to be understood within narrow economic parameters. The second is that a 'Lady Bountiful' approach is adopted whereby the relationship is reduced to prosperous Scotland sharing a small part of her bounty with her impoverished old friend Malawi. The more the dynamics move in this patronising, disempowering direction, the more they undermine the relationship of mutual respect which is the key to authentic partnership. This point was deftly made at the Scotland-Malawi conference by Matthews Chikaonda when he quoted the Malawian proverb: 'no one can shave your head in your absence.'[18]

To move beyond the donor-client model will require an engagement which is deeper and broader than that which normally obtains between the rich and poor worlds. It will need to draw on the 'very definite radicalism' which Shepperson identified as a shared characteristic of the two nations.[19] The experience of the Scotland-Malawi conference suggests that this continues to be a rich resource. In his closing address, Sir David Steel recalled the biblical injunction 'come, let us reason together'.[20] The robust quality of the debate and the manifest commitment to mutual understanding augured well.

The conference was radical in its willingness to question received wisdom and to open up new lines of analysis. Thandika Mkandawire noted that the standard approach to development is the quid pro quo: the West offers aid, provided that the recipient Governments adopt the 'good policies' and 'good governance' promoted by the Washington consensus. He went on to observe, 'what if those policies and institutions being promoted as "good" are in fact the wrong ones, or simply not feasible at the current levels of development?'[21] The more that Scotland-Malawi engagement pursues such radical questions, the more it will bring a distinctive contribution to the debate on poverty.

In order to address the pressing economic questions effectively, there is need for a much broader canvas than is usually available – a need to understand each other in all the different aspects of society and culture. Historical inspiration might be derived from David Clement Scott's monumental 1892 *Mang'anja Dictionary*, which shows how deeply some Scots had engaged with Malawian language and culture in the pre-colonial period.[23] Partnership today means Malawians forming a critical understanding of Scotland and contributing to its evolution and development.

The passion for education which is shared by the two nations can be used as a tool to inspire mutual understanding. The arts have a particular role to play – critically reading each other's literature, hearing and playing each other's music and appreciating each other's painting and sculpture. Combining depth of analysis with breadth of engagement, it may be that our two small nations can demonstrate in manifold ways the principle stated by David Clement Scott, who did so much to pioneer Scotland-Malawi relations: 'Mutual respect is the lesson we so much need to learn at this time.'[23]

Kenneth R. Ross is Chair of the Scottish Board of the Scotland-Malawi Partnership.

1. David Livingstone and Charles Livingstone, *Narrative of an Expedition to the Zambezi and its Tributaries, and of the Discoveries of Lakes Shirwa and Nyassa, 1858–1864.* London: John Murray, 1865. Andrew C. Ross, *David Livingstone: Mission and Empire.* London & New York: Hambledon and London, 2002.

2. Andrew C. Ross, *Blantyre Mission and the Making of Modern Malawi.* Blantyre: CLAIM, 1996. John McCracken, *Politics and Christianity in Malawi, 1875–1940.* Cambridge: Cambridge University Press, 1977; 2nd ed. Blantyre: CLAIM, 2000.

3. Hugh W. Macmillan, 'The Origins and Development of the African Lakes Company, 1878–1908', PhD. University of Edinburgh, 1970.

4. Ross, *Blantyre Mission*, pp. 85–104.

5. *Ibid*, pp. 109–16.

6. George A. Shepperson, 'External Factors in the Development of African Nationalism, with Particular Reference to British Central Africa'. Phylon: *The Atlanta University Review of Race and Culture*, Vol. XXII/3 (1961), pp. 207–28.

7. K. Nyamayaro Mufuka, *Missions and Politics in Malawi*. Kingston, Ontario: Limestone Press, 1977.

8. Kenneth R. Ross, 'Malawi's Peaceful Revolution 1992–94: the Role of the Church of Scotland', *Scottish Church History Society Records*, Vol. XXVII (1997), pp. 280–304.

9. Shepperson, 'External Factors' p. 212.

10. http://www.strath.ac.uk/projects/malawi

11. Memorandum and Articles of Association of the Scotland-Malawi Partnership, 2005; http://www.scotland-malawipartnership.org

12. Cooperation Agreement between Scotland and Malawi, November 2005, 'Malawi After Gleneagles: A Commission for Africa Case Study', *Report of the Scotland-Malawi Partnership Conference*, November 2005, pp. 5–6; http://www.scotland-malawipartnership.org

13. Scottish Executive News Release, 4 November 2005.

14. Register of Cross-Party Groups, Scottish Parliament.

15. Colin Cameron, Malawi Honorary Consul in Scotland, Scotland-Malawi Partnership meeting, Glasgow City Chambers, 7 February 2006.

16. 'Malawi After Gleneagles', p. 1.

17. 'International Cooperation at a Crossroads: Aid, Trade and Security in an Unequal World', United Nations Development Programme Report 2005, New York: UNDP, 2005.

18. 'Malawi After Gleneagles', p. 104.

19. Shepperson, 'External Factors', p. 212.

20. Isaiah 1:18; Sir David Steel, 'Conclusions and Recommendations from the Conference', 'Malawi After Gleneagles', p. 105.

21. 'Malawi After Gleneagles', p. 35.

22. David Clement Scott, *A Cyclopaedic Dictionary of the Mang'anja Language Spoken in British Central Africa*. Edinburgh: Church of Scotland, 1892.

23. David Clement Scott, *Life and Work in British Central Africa*, December 1897.

Multiple Visions

An Introduction to African Cinema

Lizelle Bisschoff

Despite the depth and breadth of filmmaking on the African continent, African cinema remains one of the most underrepresented cinemas on film screens around the world. Yet evocative and imaginatively original films have for decades been created by Africans on the continent. Egypt has a film industry dating back to the 1920s; films by sub-Saharan Africans emerged after independence in the 1960s. Due to the immense distribution barriers faced by African cinema, many African films are confined to one-off screenings at international film festivals and receive very limited distribution in Africa and in the West. African filmmakers struggle to make their films available to their own people; most African countries do not have adequate cinema infrastructures to service their populations and even in countries such as South Africa where these exist, the cost of a cinema ticket is often prohibitive for the majority of the population. A wealth of films has been created on the African continent – from the prolific cinemas of West Africa, including Nigeria's Nollywood, to aesthetically innovative films from North African countries and fascinating cinematic works from Guinea-Bissau, Rwanda, Namibia, and Chad. The existence of such a fertile African film production culture may be seen as something of a miracle, given the continent's ongoing socio-economic problems in the postcolonial era. However, Africans have for decades used film as a medium of self-representation, to depict their amazingly rich, diverse and complex cultures and document their daily existence. African filmmakers have taken on this challenge partly as a response to the films made on the continent by the colonial powers, which often used Africa as an exotic backdrop to tell Western stories or depicted African peoples and cultures as primitive and in need of Western intervention.

Defining African cinema is a complex task, as the continent consists of so many diverse cultures made up of multiple histories and colonial experiences. The term is often used only in relation to sub-Saharan African filmmaking, with cinema from North African countries grouped with cinema from the Arab world. Determining what constitutes the category of African cinema inevitably brings questions of authenticity and exclusion to the fore. For example, it is necessary to consider the role that Western-based filmmakers from the African diaspora play within this category, as well as the place of white filmmakers in countries such as South Africa and Zimbabwe. The international mix of finances typically involved in African feature film production, sometimes with strings attached which affect representational and artistic choices, problematises this issue further. Attempts to present a unified vision of African cinema thematically or aesthetically are very difficult, because the conception that African cinema should exclusively tell African stories in a certain way is clearly arguable. Filmmakers worldwide adopt stories from cultures other than their own, and present their own interpretative expressions of global events and histories, influenced by filmmaking practices and styles from all over the world.

The idea of a homogeneous African cinema is far too limiting when one considers the regional differences, historical forms of resistance and discursive strategies and cultural manifestations of Africa before, during and after colonisation. It is for these reasons that many African film theorists, critics and filmmakers feel most at ease with the concept of *multiple African cinemas* – a plural, heterogeneous term not situated exclusively as an alternative to or antithesis of Western cinema. Setting up a binary opposition with Western cinema in order to identify an authentically African film aesthetic conceals the facts that African filmmakers are of course exposed to film styles from all over the world, and many have received their training in the West. African cinema is not developing in isolation but as part of a worldwide phenomenon. In line with the assertion of a plurality of African cinemas, this article will give a brief overview of contemporary francophone West African filmmaking practices as well as of post-apartheid South African cinema.

Africans under French colonial rule were denied the right to film their own countries. The Laval decree of 1934 attempted to control the content of films and to minimise the creative role of Africans in film production (Diawara,

1992: 22). The first film directed by a sub-Saharan black African, *Afrique sur Seine* by Paulin S. Vieyra in 1955, about Africans living in Paris, was filmed in France because Vieyra was not allowed to film in Africa. France only started to develop African film after independence, with the creation of the Consortium Audio-visuel International (CAI). The film distribution and exhibition network left by the French colonial administration after the independence of francophone African countries as well as institutionalised support for African cinema contributed greatly to the development of national film production in these countries during the 1960s. In the 1980s, the socialist government of the Mitterrand era supported African directors, and this cultural support for francophone African cinema and other art forms continues today (although money is now also available from EU funding sources). However, many West African filmmakers criticise the paternalistic and imperialist nature of French aid to francophone African countries.

Until the early 1990s, francophone African countries were responsible for 80% of the films made across the African continent and were in this sense in a leading position in relation to many other African countries (Diawara, 1992: 34). The French companies COMACICO and SECMA controlled the distribution, exhibition and film programming of most of francophone Africa and when some countries nationalised their cinema industries after independence, the two companies refused to distribute films to these countries. Furthermore, the practice of block booking meant that directors could not show their films in their own countries and filmmakers reacted by putting pressure on their governments to nationalise distribution and film screening. West African filmmakers are still struggling to make their work available to their own people; most West African audiences are fed on a film diet of Hollywood, Bollywood and kung fu films, much cheaper for distributors to acquire than African films.

Although the economic difficulties and political instability prevalent in many West African countries make filmmaking a challenging career choice, many internationally significant filmmakers have emerged from francophone West Africa. Senegalese writer and filmmaker Ousmane Sembene was the first sub-Saharan African filmmaker to gain international recognition in the 1960s with his third film *La Noire de...* (*Black Girl*, 1966). This politically and socially committed filmmaker is now an octogenarian. His latest film, *Moolaadé* (2004), a deeply humane film about female genital mutilation, won the *Prix Un Certain Regard* at the Cannes Film Festival in 2004. Malian filmmaker Souleymane Cissé has directed half a dozen films of which *Yeelen* (1987) is undoubtedly the best-known. This visually stunning film concerns the struggle between a young man with magical powers and his sorcerer father and has won many international awards. Mauritanian director Med Hondo employed a fragmented narrative and surrealist style in his debut feature, *Soleil O* (1967), an unrepentant denouncement of colonialism. Senegalese filmmaker Djibril Diop Mambety's work is likewise groundbreaking stylistically through the non-linear juxtaposition of imagery and mixing of Western and African storytelling techniques in *Touki Bouki* (1973), a tale about two young Senegalese lovers' romanticised plan to move to France. Idrissa Ouedraogo from Burkina Faso, one of West Africa's best-known filmmakers, has to date directed more than twenty films, including *Yaaba* (1989), which won the FIPRESCI Prize at Cannes in 1989; and *Tilai* (1990), awarded the Grand Jury Prize at Cannes in 1990 and the Grand Prize at FESPACO in 1991. He also directed the Burkina Faso segment for *11'09'01 – September 11* (2002), a portmanteau film comprising interpretations of the effects of the 9/11 terrorist attacks told from different points of view around the world, which also included segments from Egyptian filmmaker Youssef Chahine and British director Ken Loach. Fellow Burkinabe filmmaker Gaston Kaboré made his first film, the highly acclaimed *Wend Kuuni* (*God's Gift*), in 1982, followed by a handful of films until the late 1990s, when Kaboré decided to direct his commitment to film towards establishing a national film school, Imagine, in Ouagadougou, built with his own money.

Diawara (1992: 140–66) distinguishes three thematic strands in West African film of which the first is the social realist tendency in which filmmakers address current socio-cultural issues through melodrama, satire, comedy and the empowerment of marginalised groups. He places most of Sembene's films in this category, alongside films of other West African filmmakers such as pioneering Burkinabe filmmaker Sekou Traoré and Malian director Cheick Oumar Sissoko. Diawara's second category consists of films that depict historical confrontation in pre-colonial Africa but also confrontation and conflict during its colonial past, and he lists Sembene's *Camp de Thiaroye* (1987), about the massacre of a group of Senegalese soldiers by the French army, as an example of this common thematic feature. Films in the third category are described by Diawara as 'Return to the Source' because their narratives depict pre-colonial traditions and customs, for example Cissé's *Yeleen*. According to Diawara African filmmakers broadly employ one of these approaches in an attempt to develop a new film language and present challenges to Western representations of Africa. Subsequent theorists have pointed out that much overlap occurs between these three categories, and, furthermore, many contemporary African films do not fit into any of them. Several theorists of African film, such as

Frank Ukadike (1994) and Melissa Thackway (2003), attempt to formulate the theoretical groundings for a uniquely Africa film aesthetic in the oral tradition of African storytelling. However, these new film languages certainly bear similarities with filmmaking outside of Africa, and rather than viewing African films in a vacuum, it should be considered how existing Western filmic influences are being adapted and transformed into appropriated versions and varieties by African filmmakers and writers.

The diversity of not only West African cinema, but cinema from the whole continent, is evident at FESPACO (*Festival Panafricain du Cinéma et de la Télévision de Ouagadougou*), the biggest festival of African film in the world which takes place biennially in the capital city of Burkina Faso. Despite being one of the poorest countries in the world, Burkina Faso has established a prolific and prominent film industry. The first FESPACO took place in 1969 and today more than half a million visitors from all over the world flock to Ouagadougou to take part in this week-long celebration of African film. The festival includes multiple screenings of over a hundred African films in the city's many cinemas as well as a film and television market. The local population enthusiastically takes part in the events, supporting the directors and actors heralded as national heroes in Burkina.

Alongside FESPACO, the Pan African Federation of Filmmakers (*Federation Panafricaine des Cineastes* – FEPACI) was created in 1969 in Algiers, with the purpose of encouraging the setting up of national organisations to support African film production and distribution. Their manifesto described a need for the emergence of new aesthetic styles and genres such as semi-documentaries and didactic fictional films, with the purpose of denouncing colonialism and combating the economic and cultural alienation of independent countries in respect of the West (Barlet, 1996). Their political aspirations have since been expanded to include the urgent requirement to create economically viable national film industries alongside the use of film as an activist tool in the continuing struggle against Western cultural and economic imperialism.

One of the most important new trends in West African filmmaking is the emergence of female filmmakers. The 2005 FESPACO included a number of fiction feature films by African women, who are hugely underrepresented in the film industry as directors, as is the case all over the world. Burkinabe director Fanta Regina Nacro, one of West Africa's best-known female filmmakers, showcased her first fiction feature, *La Nuit de la Vérité* (The Night of Truth, 2004) in the official competition. The film is set in a fictional African country and deals with the traumatic process of reaching inter-ethnic reconciliation, a theme echoed not only all over Africa in the case of countries such as Rwanda, Liberia and Sierra Leone, but also in other parts of the world such as Israel, Bosnia and Yugoslavia. The 2005 FESPACO also included the first fiction feature, *Sous la Clarté de la Lune* (*Under the Moon's Light*, 2004), by emerging female Burkinabe filmmaker Appoline Traoré, mentored by Idrissa Ouedraogo. The film depicts the quest of an African mother to reclaim her mixed-race daughter who was taken away at birth and raised in France. Thematically this film employs a recurrent motif of African cinema – the tension between traditional African culture and modernity. Produced digitally, it is part of the digital revolution currently taking place in world filmmaking. African filmmakers are increasingly making use of this new technology, a low-cost, viable alternative to traditional filmmaking practices and a crucial development which might just signify a major shift towards the expansion of African film production and distribution.

Unlike the birth of francophone African cinema which was postponed by French colonial policy, cinema in South Africa is more than one hundred years old – South Africa is often cited as one of the first countries worldwide to marvel at the invention of the moving image. However, the history of the oldest film industry in Africa, as with the history of the country at large, is a skewed and scattered legacy full of omissions and silences left by the absent voices of those oppressed and silenced during firstly a rule of foreign colonial powers, followed by the rule of a white minority. Because of South Africa's disjointed history – out of sync with the historical patterns of colonisation, freedom struggles and eventual independence that shaped the modern era for most other African countries – South African cinema during apartheid is excluded from historical and theoretical discussions of African film as a whole. If cinema is regarded as a manifestation of South African cultural history, the omitted narratives shape as much a socio-historical and cultural account of the audio-visual medium as the dominant, white voices of the apartheid era do. The unrepresentative nature of those who controlled the means of image creation and production is one of the factors burdening the development and making of a contemporary South African cinema.

A traceable tradition of radical activist black filmmaking failed to develop in South Africa during apartheid. Film was not used as a political activist tool from within the country in the way that it was used to depict, document and support the liberation struggles in lusophone African countries (Mozambique, Angola and Guinea-Bissau). Although a long tradition of activist theatre, as well as the use of music as a consciousness-raising tool, can be traced in locations like Hillbrow, Sophiatown and Newtown in Johannesburg, the medium of film, expensive and inaccessible to most black South Africans during apartheid, was not taken up as a weapon in the struggle against apartheid. 'South Africa, site of the most repressive society in the world, is unfortunately not the base for the most militant liberationist film indicative of oppressed societies', states Ukadike (1994: 223).

By the end of apartheid, the film industry was left fragmented and economically unstable, after being treated for decades by the government as an industry that should provide light entertainment at maximum financial gain, rather than as a creative industry with potential for cultural expression or self-reflexivity. But the last twelve years have seen, as in so many other socio-cultural, -political and -economic spheres, massive policy and structural changes as well as a transformation in the country's national, regional and international relationships. The re-integration of South Africa into the continent's future is exemplified by the ideology of an African Renaissance, promoted by the South African government along with the governments of other African countries. In April 2006 the South African Department of Arts and Culture and the National Film and Video Foundation (NFVF), in association with the Pan African Federation of Filmmakers (FEPACI) hosted the annual General Congress of FEPACI as well as an accompanying African Film Summit in Johannesburg. This event constitutes a major realignment of the South African film industry, as well as in the development of African cinema, previously centred on West Africa.

The processes of regional, continental and international reintegration that South Africa is going through have many implications for the film industry, not least because the South African government as well as industry and commercial players are committed to encouraging film production and exhibition for its commercial, cultural and educational benefits. These different agendas informing and shaping policy making and film production, exhibition and distribution structures in South Africa clash at times, as in most countries the world over struggling to establish and nurture independent, artistically innovative and national cinemas against the capitalist onslaught of commercialism and Hollywood domination. Although the past twelve years have seen growing institutional and governmental support for the local film industry, especially encouraging black filmmakers who did not have access to the industry under apartheid, it is often felt that change in South Africa is coming too slowly, that not enough black and previously disadvantaged citizens have been empowered yet, and that many institutions, including the film industry, are still being unfairly dominated by white South Africans.

The fragmented film industry inherited by the new ANC government at the demise of apartheid in 1994 has undergone extensive structural changes in terms of funding, training, production, exhibition and distribution. The commercial film industry has grown vigorously and continues to do so, with film production ranging from commercials and short films to feature-length films, fiction and documentary. According to South African film theorist Martin Botha (2003) some of the most significant trends shaping the South African film industry are: the emergence of black film talent; the alignment and consolidation of the independent film production sector; surges of media donor funding especially for the development of documentaries; international demand for South African conservation and wildlife productions; and a strong recent South African participation in international markets. To this should be added the increasing use of digital technology.

The production boom that South African cinema has undergone recently, as well as the international success and recognition that South African films are increasingly enjoying is certainly something to celebrate, but it should also be considered how popular these films are in the country itself. Despite the massive growth in local production over the last five years, only a fraction of the South African public attends cinema regularly, and they see mostly mainstream Hollywood films. The commercial realities of the film industry in South Africa are shaped by the difficulties in establishing an economically viable indigenous national industry amongst audiences who have for decades been fed on overseas imports and who regarded local films as rare oddities mostly inferior to international products. To view film and television as crucial forms of cultural and artistic expression as well as an educational tool often conflicts with the economic considerations of distributors and broadcasters. It is important, in this regard, to distinguish the purpose of alternative, artistically innovative or even 'radical' filmmaking, intended to raise social awareness, educate and celebrate creative and artistic expression, from the commercial model of cinema concerned primarily with financial return. The main film distributors in South Africa, Ster Kinekor and Nu Metro, are generally not very keen to take a chance on local films or to commit to developing new audiences for local products, which would disrupt income streams and inevitably result in a time period during which profits would be low or non-existent. South African films are released in local cinemas with varied box office success, and, as is echoed all over the continent, many players in the South African film industry also feel that to improve this situation local distributors have to start believing in local films. It is suggested that quotas for local film exhibition in cinemas should be set up and enforced, and a substantial percentage of the box office return from foreign film exhibition should be fed back into the local industry.

Previously unheard stories and repressed voices are gradually emerging in film and television locally, with South African films also starting to enjoy international critical acclaim. The year 2005 in particular saw a number of international breakthroughs, with South Africa receiving its first Academy Award Nomination in the Foreign Film category for *Yesterday* (Darrell Roodt, 2004), a film about the effects of HIV/AIDS on a young Zulu mother. In the same year Zola Maseko's *Drum* (2004), a fictional interpretation of a *Drum* magazine journalist's involvement in the anti-apartheid struggles of 1950s Sophiatown, won the grand prize at FESPACO, a surprising choice given the francophone dominated character of the festival. *Drum* magazine, which was run by a number of prominent anti-apartheid journalists and intellectuals, was an important mouthpiece against the oppressive and dehumanising consequences of apartheid and Maseko stylishly recreates the political and cultural vibrancy of Sophiatown, where most *Drum* journalists lived and frequented jazz bars. Demolished in the 1950s under the nationalist apartheid government's Group Areas Act, Sophiatown remains a poignant symbol of South Africa's troubled past. Mark Dornford-May's *U-Carmen e-Khayelitsha* (*Carmen in Khayelitsha*, 2005), based on the famous opera by Bizet, sung entirely in Xhosa and set in the Cape township of Khayelitsha, won the Golden Bear Award at the 2005 Berlin International Film Festival. The film employs a number of astute cultural translations in order to Africanise the opera and comment on post-apartheid township life. Not insignificantly, the first feature film by a black South African female filmmaker saw the light in 2005 as well: Maganthrie Pillay's *34 South* is a road movie addressing issues of identity in the new South Africa. Gavin Hood's *Tsotsi* (2005), based on the Athol Fugard novel of the same title about a Soweto gangster, has swept up a plethora of international film festival awards during 2005 and 2006, and won the Academy Award for Best Foreign Film earlier this year. Fugard's novel, written in the late 1950s, is transposed into post-apartheid South Africa in Hood's screenplay and, although the film has been criticised for its Hollywood-like narrative and style, it has also been favourably compared to Fernando Meirelles' *City of God* (2002), set in a violent neighbourhood of Rio de Janeiro.

The feature films and documentaries produced in South Africa over the last few years show that multiple genres and themes are being explored – from post-apartheid dramas and struggle stories to popular comedies and musicals. Although South Africa's history of overt racialisation through racial classification still provides impetus for many current films, according to Masilela & Balseiro (2003: 5) the transition to a democracy marks a shift from an emphasis on racial politics in South African film criticism, to other areas of concern, for example questions of gender, sexuality and class. Issues of identity have been one of the driving forces behind filmmaking in South Africa over the past few years and political themes dealing with South Africa's past and present have occurred in many audio-visual productions. In particular, young, previously disadvantaged emerging filmmakers are being empowered through training and funding opportunities to make their voices heard and tell their personal stories because the audio-visual medium is seen as an important democratising device in reflecting on and shaping individual and cultural identity within post-apartheid South Africa. This statement, in fact, appears to be true for the whole of Africa, where cinema has become an important tool for cultural expression in the post-colonial era.

Works Cited

Balseiro, Isabel & Masilela, Ntongela (eds). *To Change Reels: Film and Film Culture in South Africa*. Detroit: Wayne State University Press, 2003.

Barlet, Olivier. *African Cinema: Decolonizing the Gaze*. London & New York: Zed Books Ltd, 1996.

Botha, Martin. 'The Song Remains the Same: The Struggle for a South African Film Audience.' Available from: www.fru.co.za/resources/essay.php?uid=22

Diawara, Manthia. *African Cinema: Politics & Culture*. Bloomington & Indianapolis: Indiana University Press, 1992.

Thackway, Melissa. *Africa Shoots Back: Alternative Perspectives in Sub-Saharan Francophone African Film*. Oxford: James Currey, 2003.

Ukadike, Frank N. *Black African Cinema*. Berkeley, Los Angeles, London: University of California Press, 1994.

Part II

Dear Honourable Member

Dear Honourable Member

Gabriel Gidi

It has been a long time since we saw you in the constituency. We last saw you on the day that you hosted the victory celebration party at the business centre. This was soon after your election victory in 2000. It was such a wonderful party that for once in the history of our dry area people had food to the fill. We remember Chinyoka's antics on that day as he recited the praise poetry of your totem.

But we digress. The purpose of this letter is to update you on certain of the developments in our constituency. It may come as a surprise that we have been able to write this letter to you in English. As a group of illiterate elders we had to ask Chinyama's son to write the letter as we dictated the words to him. You may remember him. He is the university boy who recited a revolutionary poem at your last rally at Sikombingo Growth Point. He is still unemployed so we thought he could employ his BA in helping us to write a letter to you. We only hope that he is honestly translating what we are telling him.

But again we digress. The letter serves to tell you that things have not improved since we voted you into power. As you are aware that our area is dry and produces very little food, we were pinning our hopes on your promises for dams and water for irrigation. We were excited when you promised that you would ensure that the water pipeline from the big river to our north would finally be built. However, up to now we still have not seen the dam or the pipeline. The project had been on the drawing board for many years when we elected you. We had lost hope but your fervent promises ignited a new hope in us. The hope is, however, fading as we realise that your parliament days for the current term are slowly drawing to an end without any significant progress in the matter. Mhinyapinya, who was our representative on the project, has since died. His relatives say he died of hunger. We hope you can come and explain what happened to the energetic, enthusiastic and caring Member of Parliament we elected in 2000. We used to rely on donors who came with food but ever since we told them to go away because they were corrupting our people with bad politics we have had so many people succumbing to hunger in the last two years. We believe that our government which cares for us will come to our rescue. If you do not come to us we will perish.

The roads have remained dusty and full of gullies and potholes. The last bus to use this road was the ZUPCO bus that brought the Border Gezi youths to your victory party. There has not been a bus service in this area for ten years. This is a perennial problem which we hoped you would help solve. People walk fifteen, some even twenty, kilometres to the nearest bus. Kambanji Bus Service has said it will only return when the roads have been repaired. The bridge on Rwenje River which was damaged by Cyclone Eline-induced rains six years ago has still not been repaired. We were happy to elect a Member of Parliament with vast experience in the civil service and several businesses. We felt that with a man who owns several top of the range Mercedes and BMW cars we would not go wrong. The urgency with which you constituted a Constituency Development Committee promised action – immediate action. But up to now we are still waiting. We are not blaming you for any of these things but only reminding you that your constituents are still waiting.

The nearest clinic to us is fifteen kilometres into Sigola's area which is under MP Pachedu. As you know that our area is a malaria zone there is need to have a health centre close to the people. It is not easy for the elderly and the sick to walk to a clinic that far. The bricks that you asked people to make so that we would build a clinic in this area have been at the site since two years ago. Our fear is that they may start disappearing. Only yesterday they caught Chimombe's son with a scotch cart load of the bricks. We have already put in place a committee of builders, carpenters and other workers ready to start work on the clinic. They are only waiting for the cement, roofing materials and the food that you promised. We trust you are going to bring these things soon.

We are only ten months to the next election Comrade MP and we feel that you need to come to the people now. We have always voted for your party because we believe it is a people's party. You are the second MP after

Comrade Chivende to represent us in parliament. You will remember that our constituency registered the highest number of votes for the party during both the 2000 parliamentary election and in the presidential elections that followed. The people of this constituency love the party. Many of them have never voted for any other party since independence. But there are disturbing developments here, Comrade MP. The people are hearing things.

First there is a young man who has been coming here telling people that he wants to be the Member of Parliament. His name is Max Kutsanzira. He belongs to the party. They call him 'Doctor' but they say his 'doctoring' has nothing to do with curing people. His campaigners in the constituency say that he knows so much about governments, politics and democracy. They say he teaches these things at the big university in Harare. He has been telling people that you have failed them and that you do not care about them, which is why you do not come here any more. He is addressing people at beer parties and at funerals telling them that he is the best man to take over from you. Some of the things he is saying are so true that it is very difficult to convince the people that he is wrong. Like we said earlier on, the people have not seen you in a very long time. Please come to us before the people have been completely corrupted.

Then there is Sunungurai Zvenyika who has also come with a different gospel. Sunungurai is Zvenyika's son who has been working in South Africa for several years. You do not need to be told anything about Zvenyika because he is the man who has been giving you competition in business at the Growth Point. The people say that your businesses have not been doing too well. But this is not important because this Sunungurai is becoming a threat to you and the party. He has also been telling the people that he is back to save the people from the corrupt and negligent rule of the party. He says he wants to be the Member of Parliament representing the new party. He has been teaching us to do the slogan with an open palm and asking us to '*chinja maitiro*'. This is all so new for the people here that many of the young ones are excited. One of Sunungurai's advantages is that he is now resident in the Constituency. Since he came back from South Africa he has taken over the running of his father's businesses at the Growth Point. He is telling the people that the era of absentee, corrupt Members of Parliament is gone and that a new era is dawning if the people vote for his party. He has taken to listing all the unfulfilled promises whenever he is addressing people who come to the bar at the hotel. He has also been talking to people in churches and they seem to be listening to him. We are not sure what to do with him because his message is so new and refreshing. We still want the party but this new party is exciting people. Is it okay if we join it? The people just so love this new thing that some have started putting on T-shirts with this party's logo. We are afraid that when you come there may not be anyone for you. Those who will not join this new party will obviously follow Max. We are concerned because as it is nobody is talking about you. It is as if you do not exist anymore. May be the people are justified because you have not been seen and they are like sheep without a shepherd. Sheep will follow any shepherd if the good shepherd is nowhere to be seen. Please Comrade MP, come before all is lost. The greatest threat is this Sunungurai and his open palm message. The people are mesmerised.

Yours truly,
Elders of Sikombingo

Aciro's Song

Jackee Budesta Batanda

A voice pierced through my door made of the USA oil tins I got from the World Food Programme every three months. Aciro was crying. It was a cry that started as a muffled sob, cautious and then slowly gained momentum. Sometimes it chortled like an old Peugeot that had run out of fuel. Tonight, it sounded clear like the church bell that rang at the makeshift church in the camp calling us to pray to a God who had abandoned us.

Aciro cried a lot these days. She had been crying since her daughter Loretta went out to collect raw mangos and never returned. We had waited for her like we did each time she had stealthily left the camp with other women foraging for food because the relief food was insufficient.

I used to join them on these escapades. We took the winding dirt road that led from the camp of hunger through shrubs into abandoned gardens bursting with food growing wildly because no one lived in the villages anymore. I used to walk in the single file of young women, as we made our way through the grass, laughing carefully like we were afraid that the wind would carry our voices back to the Major, who would send his guards after us. We laughed and talked about everything but the danger we knew lay ahead. We avoided talking about a probable rebel or government soldiers ambush. Instead we talked about how we used to cultivate sesame seeds, millet and sorghum and how we had made sheanut butter. We imagined we would find our ancestors had magically cultivated our gardens in the night. But that was only a folktale our mothers had recited to us, when as children we had believed that the spirit of fire and not the wind blowing through the grass thatched huts, controlled the dancing flames.

I joined in these escapades until I lost my legs to a landmine. 'You are lucky to be alive,' everyone said. 'Lubanga took pity on you,' they added and the congregation at the makeshift church prayed for my speedy recovery. But I was angry at the God they praised for my survival for letting me live.

Once some photographers and women from a Women's organisation in the big city came to our camp. The women stepped out of four-wheel drive cars accompanied by a military convoy. They walked in high-heeled shiny shoes that left tiny holes on the soggy ground. Their strong perfume filled the camp, suffocating the stench. We envied them. Their organisation dealt with women and children in areas of armed conflict, they said. They had come to find women who would need surgical operations and counselling to enable them lead a normal life again. And we wondered what a normal life was because each day we lived on the sleeve of insanity was another taunt we threw at death. They had said they would take our stories back to the big city to the Parliamentarians. They said that peace would come flowing through the camp like the early morning Acoli-pii sunshine.

We had smiled through our yellowed teeth and had hovered around them like little children who had been promised éclair toffees by the young men that sat around the God's Grace bar drinking malwa and playing board games to pass time. We wondered where God's grace went because it surely didn't live in Acoli-pii. The Women had promised to collect food and clothes for us while we hoped they would bring us peace. We had sung Aciro's song.

You've cut off my hand
Go on and get famous for it
You've cut off my lips so that I cannot talk
Now go and get famous for it.

The Women had applauded us and recorded Aciro's song. It would be called 'A Lingering Pain' (like our lives in the camp, they forgot to add). They would send it to organisations around the world to put pressure on our government to end the war. That was three years ago. Three years ago Aciro's daughter Loretta was still alive. Loretta whose bright smile made it seem like the sun rose from her mouth in Acoli-pii. Three years ago, nobody knew that she would one day leave the camp never to return.

The day the Women came had been like the Thursday November morning

I had lost my legs to a landmine. It had been a hot steamy day, with the sun threatening to burn us to ashes. We had left camp, because we hadn't received food in a long time and we had grown tired of boiling unripe papaya for our meals. We had taken the footpath behind the Major's hut. Everyone had passed the spot safely but my legs had veered off the path a little and I stepped on the landmine.

That was the day I had stopped going to search for food and Loretta had promised to always bring me provisions. That is why when she hadn't come back by the time the sun was fading into the horizon like the last note in a song; we had started to grow restless. Aciro had asked me if they had gone further today and had to walk a longer distance. I had nodded in assurance even though I had felt something grow in my throat. There had been a lump in my throat after my parents had died in a rebel ambush. It started to disappear when Aciro and Loretta had taken me under their care. Now the lump was growing back and I knew it was Loretta bringing it back. I had sighed and looked down avoiding Aciro's questioning eyes. I hadn't wanted her to see the truth in my eyes as it raced through my brains. So I had cleared my throat and said in a squeaky voice, 'they surely have travelled a long distance today.' She had nodded and I had added, 'they will be back with the moon tonight.'

She had crouched against her hut and cuddled her grandchildren. The lump in my throat was starting to spill out of my mouth. Aciro had untied the orange kitenge wrapper from her waist and had covered the children. She had sat with her right hand cupping her cheek like a woman in mourning.

The moon didn't bring Loretta home that night. I avoided her eyes when she asked, 'Loretta will come back with another moon tonight, won't she?'

We both knew that Loretta was in trouble. The lump in my throat was choking me. Aciro looked to me for reassurance that her daughter would return. She clasped my hand. Her roughened hands felt like scales on my arm. She shook me strongly and asked again, 'Will Loretta come back with another moon tonight?' I shook my head. The moon hang in the sky like a big neon lamp. She tightened the grip on my hand. I wanted to tell her that Loretta would return to us and we would smile and laugh together and listen to our transistor radio blaring songs on Mega FM. Songs that took us on journeys to places where lovers broke up and made up. Songs that took us to the big city with the song 'eno city Kampala', this is Kampala City. Then we sang along and nodded our heads in tune to the music that entered our bodies and made us want to run under the Jambula tree in the middle of the camp and sing at the top of our lungs for everyone to hear.

'Min, I don't know,' I said.

She sighed and sucked in her breath. Lines had developed on her forehead. Under the moonlight, I noticed the greys around her temples. I wanted to say something that would make her feel better. But you don't tell a mother who is anxiously waiting for a daughter who has disappeared in the wind that something will work out. You don't tell her the truth she is intentionally ignoring although you know it is biting at her conscience. And you know that she knows. So you join in the forlorn hope that the lost daughter will rise with the sun because the sun rises in Acoli-pii.

When the first women who had gone out to look for water returned wailing, I was sitting outside the hut. The sun was making slow steps on the ground. The thatch roof created a good shade for me. Aciro sat in the doorway where she had spent the night waiting for Loretta. She had struggled to get up and had landed heavily on the ground. I had crawled to her but she was up again before I could get to her. She ran towards the voices. I had crawled slowly after her.

'Where is my Loretta?' she had cried shaking the women near her, looking them in the eyes. I think she was searching for a little hope that she could cling to. Someone had taken her aside and calmly told her that the rebels had ambushed the young women.

I don't remember what happened next. Perhaps Aciro screamed so loudly the wind must have carried her voice to the bloodstained ground where her daughter lay. Or maybe she fainted. She might have repeatedly hit the person who had told her the news she had known all night long. Someone later told me that she had been taken to the makeshift dispensary where the camp nurse had given her some tranquilisers.

Later when I was alone, I tried to imagine how Loretta had met her end. I wished that I had been there when Loretta and the women met the rebels. Pressing my eyes shut, I ground my teeth and the prayer on my lips was for death to come gently and take me too.

Aciro came back from the dispensary on a Sunday. It was the first time she didn't go to the makeshift church in the camp. It was also the day Aciro stopped singing in the church choir. We had sat silently outside the hut and watched her grandchildren playing in the distance. It seemed like our lives had stopped flowing. We missed Loretta. She had asked me, 'Do you feel a stone sitting in your heart?' I had nodded. She had said she felt the same way. I wanted to say there was a lump in my throat but my tongue was heavy. 'It's Loretta sitting in our hearts,' she said and squinted her eyes. She had developed that squint after Loretta hadn't come back to the camp. It was like she didn't want anyone to really look into her eyes. Perhaps she was hiding the sorrow that had now become a part of her, like the little black mole under her left eye.

Aciro later told me that her life was like a sad song that made her want to cry. She had stopped singing in the church so as not to sing out the little strength left within her frail body. So she sat outside her hut like she was waiting for Loretta. Sometimes she sniffed a little, or her sobs seeped through the metallic door like they did tonight.

I curled up and listened to Aciro's voice. It grew into me. I couldn't cry. I had cried out all my tears when I lost my legs. My eyes were dried up like the stream outside the camp. I listened to the voice that reminded me of our loss. Aciro made me sad. I let out a muffled sob. I remembered the Women from the big city who came three years ago and promised us peace. I blamed them for Loretta's death. I blamed them for Aciro's crying. What happened to Aciro's song? I had forgotten the words. Three years was a long time to remember things. It was better to forget the things of the past so that you could live on.

But I still remembered the landmine. I still remembered that Aciro cried because her daughter was dead. I still remembered many things. Some things refused to go away and returned like the night edging out the day. They came each day and forced me to remember. The memories swelled onto me and stuck in my mind like an embarrassing birthmark.

In the morning, I crawled and sat outside my hut. I saw Aciro and discreetly watched her eyes, searching for signs of the previous night's crying. I was afraid to meet her eyes. She turned on her transistor radio and placed it on the ground between us. The voice coming from it was shaky because the Tiger batteries were weak. We watched the sun sweeping through the camp and drying the shit mounds that littered the ground. A red hen passed near our radio, almost knocking it over. Aciro shooed it away. She broke the silence.

'The fighting is destroying the peace,' she said. I nodded.

She added that Loretta visited her dream the previous night. She alleged Loretta was fine and would reappear with the moon tonight.

'She knows we are hungry. Just you wait,' she affirmed, 'my Loretta will come back to me this evening.'

She turned to me and smiled. A smile that hang on the edge of her mouth. I wanted to shake her hard and tell her that Loretta was dead. Isn't that why she had buried three stones behind her hut to mark Loretta's grave? Hadn't we prayed for her spirit when the church congregation came to pray for us? I wanted to tell her that Loretta would not return with the moon tonight or tomorrow night because she hadn't returned for six months. Hadn't we asked Loretta not to rest but to haunt her killers? I wanted to ask her but the voice was tied round the lump in my throat. Instead of telling her to pull herself together if not for her sake but for her grandchildren, I sat around with my head hanging down, ashamed that I could not bring myself to tell her the truth.

So I tried to remember Aciro whose melodious voice was capable of making Miriam Makeba jealous. I avoided this Aciro who made up stories of her dead daughter during the day and cried in the night for the same daughter. This Aciro, who lived a lie, because she had numbed her senses to the truth. I forgot this Aciro, who now hang around the God's Grace makeshift bar, and watched the young men that played board games and drank malwa brew. This Aciro who chased away the *ojuu* insects that sat on the beer pots in exchange for 'just a little sip' and came staggering to her hut in the night. But the drink didn't make her forget her daughter. It made her cry even more because she felt the solitude in the night. It made her squirm in longing for the end of the life she said was a sad song that made her want to cry.

Aciro stopped waiting for Loretta to return and started singing again. Not in the church choir. A bar singer. She sang the songs as they came to her head. She sang at the makeshift bar, where the young men and sometimes the soldiers came to hear her sing their lives in her songs. Her voice rang through the camp and carried her pain into the hearts of her audience. She was a star in the camp, a live voice the people could listen to instead of the artificial voices that came through the transistor radios in the camp. She gave music a body.

But later in the evening, she came to my hut and told me there was a song that made her cry for her daughter. The song she wanted to sing but could not find the words. I reminded her of the song she sang when the Women from the big city came to our camp promising us peace. She said that song reminded her of Loretta. 'Nobody wants to remember their loss,' she said in a voice husky from singing at the bar, 'but I've a loss that sits in my heart,' she added and punched her chest. 'Right here and it's growing heavy like the stone that sits in our hearts,'

I echoed her words, 'it's Loretta sitting in our hearts.' She nodded.

Weeks later when Aciro came knocking at my door and announced that she could now sing the song that had been nagging her because she had found the words, I impatiently asked her to sing it. Perhaps the song would conjure Loretta's spirit, I thought. And when she opened her mouth and the words came tumbling out, I was sure Aciro had found her song.

It is Well in My Soul

Wame Molefhe

Lebo, her friend, was dead and buried.

Sethunya was relieved she had been spared having to bury Lebo. She had been in England, far away enough from Botswana for Lebo's family and friends not to question why she did not attend the funeral.

She should not have asked how Lebo died. She had always found the unbridled curiosity that made people probe the cause of a person's death intrusive, unwarranted and in bad taste. But like a curious child who asks 'but why' over and over again, something deep inside compelled her to ask what killed Lebo. She did not remember her exact words but she must have said 'What did she die of?' That is how polite people usually enquired.

Those who were adept at ferreting out other people's information reported that Lebo died of a short illness. They trooped off to her funeral, in their Sunday best, to the 3,000-people-strong village from which she came. They examined those who had been her friends, and friends of friends. They searched their faces for signs of frailty. Upon their return, they told all who would listen that they had buried dear Lebo. 'Shame,' they said, 'Lebo really suffered.'

Sethunya studied Lebo's funeral programme. It was typed on plain, flimsy, A4 paper, folded in half. It was the kind of paper reserved for people who could only afford the bronze, not platinum, funeral plan. The bronze plan guaranteed you 100 programmes, some groceries, basic coffin and hearse.

Platinum promised flowers, albeit plastic, 300 glossy A3 size embossed paper programmes, a casket, a choice between a black or white hearse, and other frills. So, the stories were true, Sethunya thought, Lebo died alone – a pauper.

The funeral programme was all Sethunya had left of Lebo. Lebo's badly printed face stared out at her from the front page.

Kelebonye Lefatshe
Born: 12 January 1975
Died: 9 January 2006
Buried: 15 January 2006

Lebo must have been twentyish when the picture was taken but she already had the look. It was a look that got men – old, young, black, white, tripping over each other in a frenzied race to be the one to win Lebo's favour. Miss Kedumetse, their form two religious education teacher called it the Jezebel look. She had peered at Lebo, over her thin glasses, pursed her lips disapprovingly and hissed, 'Jezebel', with the accent on the second syllable.

The names of the speakers were typed on the inside pages. Mr Nthobatsang, Lebo's uncle, had spoken as Lebo's family representative. She knew him well. He must have worn his wedding-cum-funeral suit. That charcoal, double-breasted suit had been pressed so often the white pinstripes had all but faded into the greyness. The jacket had two vents at the back which gaped open, stretched by a rotund rear. He always wore his once white, now off-white shirt with the suit. Its collar was slightly frayed but always starched. She could almost hear his gravelly voice saying slowly, '*Ngwana wa rona o re tlogetse re solohetse go le gontsi mo go ene. E ne e le ngwana yo o lorato, yo o utlwang.*' Like a benevolent uncle, he would have described Lebo as a loving and obedient niece – snatched away before her time.

The programme had 'friend' written by hand. The name of the friend had been tippexed out. Her name must have been written there, before the family was told she was overseas. She should have spoken. After all, she and Lebo had shared so much. She wondered who had stood in for her. Neoyame, maybe... But then again, probably not. The label, 'friend of Lebo', had an ominous ring to it.

The *mooki*, the person who nursed the deceased, was listed as third to speak. It was Lebo's aunt, MmaDomi. MmaDomi was a councillor, nursing aspirations of becoming a Member of Parliament at the next elections. At the last funeral Sethunya attended, people had squirmed in their chairs as MmaDomi revealed intimate details of the deceased's illness. Personal and confidential details which really should have remained in the person's medical file. When angry relatives confronted her afterwards, MmaDomi said she had meant no harm. We need to speak about these things, she explained. Still, Lebo hoped, this time, MmaDomi had chosen respect for the dead over sensationalism. Whichever way, the *mooki* always ended with: 'This is how our child died. May her soul rest in peace,' or words to that effect.

Sethunya hoped there had been a priest to bury Lebo. But Lebo had never been big on church. She maintained that her relationship with God needed no intermediary. She was tickled by the antics of some avowed believers. She said she did not want to wear her Christian-ness on the outside – to mask a pitch, black heart.

Oh yes, we say we should not speak ill of the dead. But there are those who defy our mores. They dig deep to uncover skeletons, buried under skeletons. They weave tales of wickedness, laced with innuendo, tinged with conjecture. We shake our heads disapprovingly but listen attentively, afraid we might hear our names mentioned. Oh, yes, these tales titillate us. We take comfort in knowing we are not as bad as the Lebos of this world. Such an evil, duplicitous people we are.

Truth be told, Sethunya was not sad Lebo was dead. Sometimes, as she tossed alone on her king-sized bed in the middle of the night, she wondered how life without Lebo would be. She wished for Lebo's prince to come and whisk her away to *Lentswe la Baratani*, 'Lovers' Hill,' where folklore said lovers went and never returned. The truth was that she hated Lebo but she had not wanted Lebo's knight in shining armour to be a short illness without a name.

Sometimes, she got angry when she thought of Lebo. Anger festered inside her, like a sore that refused to heal despite repeated applications of gentian violet. Other times, thinking of Lebo frightened her. The fear chilled her fingers and toes on a 39-degree November afternoon. It made her forehead feel hot to the touch on a wintry June morning. It crept stealthily up on her as she slept and made her sit bolt upright in the middle of the night. The fear used to come only at night. But she could feel it closing in on her she sat in her office, dwarfed by her man-sized mahogany desk.

She felt the fear in her chest as her heart pounded against her ribs. An arrhythmic, pulsating beat surged to her head and banged against her temples. Voices joined in. 'Lebo is dead. Lebo is gone. May her soul rest in peace,' they chorused. Sethunya made the sign of the cross with her right hand. She pressed her hands together in prayer. Her hands felt clammy. Fear filled her bladder. She strode to the ladies.

'*Dumela, mme.*' The tea-lady's respectful greeting startled her. It reminded her of who she was. Women at her workplace thought she was invincible. Sethunya looked up, shortened her gait and swayed her hips from side to side as she walked down the corridor. She entered the bathroom. Locked the door behind her and looked into the mirror.

Hazel eyes, stared back at her. Contacts did that. Her eyebrows were plucked into perfect arches. Midnight blue mascara thickened her lashes. She turned her head slightly, to the left. Her teeth were white, straight and even now. The product of braces and bleach. During her last visit to the US she finally found a shade of foundation that did not make her skin look like day-old-cow-liver. She applied her make up religiously, every morning; touched it up at lunchtime. The result was a blemish-free skin and a nose with a homemade point. This was not the face of a woman gripped by irrepressible fear.

She wiped a bead of sweat off the tip of her minimised nose. Another appeared on her forehead, then another and another. Rivulets of sweat ran down her back, making her silk blouse cling to her skin. Her underarms felt wet. She closed her eyes to stem the rising panic. Images, buried deep down where no one could see were resurrected. They waltzed behind her closed eyes. Two silhouettes – of a man and woman. The woman's dress billowed in the air and swirled high above her knees. The man held out his hand to her. He twirled her round and round. Her dress flew off. The two came together. Their bare bodies twisted and turned. They writhed and cried out and the macabre dance began again. Lebo. Lebo and Ntsimane, Sethunya's husband. There was a knock on the door. All at once the images disappeared. She was in control again.

She flushed the toilet, unlocked the door and strode back to her office. She sank into her soft leather, high-back, executive swivel chair and swung it round. She opened the window to Gaborone city. Blaring taxi horns. A wedding procession. A black hearse crawling through the traffic. She banged the window shut and turned her chair to her desk. Her in-tray was overflowing. She plunged in and worked steadily. Right through lunch… 6:00 pm. The building was deserted. Most people fled the office at 4:30 pm precisely.

It was 7:00 pm when she reached home. She turned on the TV. 'Petrol prices will go up at midnight. Inflation rates reach all time high. Water restrictions are to be enforced. The AIDS conference was officially opened by….' She switched off the TV and went into the kitchen. The fridge was empty. She got back into the car again and drove to Riverwalk Mall to get something to eat. Lebo had always teased her about her appetite. She always ate. Healthily. Heartily. A subconscious attempt to build up her reserves, perhaps?

'What can I get you, mma? ' asked the waiter.

'T-bone, phaleche, steamed vegetables… and malva pudding,' she ordered.

'How done?'

'Excuse me?' Sethunya looked up at the waiter.

'I'm asking how done? The steak, Madame.'

'Oh. Well done, please.' Sethunya struggled to suppress a smile. It was wiped off her face by a familiar voice.

'Hi Sethunya! I didn't see you at the funeral.'

'I wasn't there. '

'Eish, poor Lebo. Such as shame.'

'Yes. A shame,' Sethunya echoed.

Sethunya looked at the speaker. Botshelo – with a nubile, young thing clinging onto his arm. As they walked away she wondered absentmindedly if they always used condoms. Then she reprimanded herself. That little girl might very well be his daughter. Botshelo had been best man at her wedding seven years ago. Lebo – had been her maid of honour.

But now Lebo had died of 'a short illness.' Botswana's euphemism for AIDS. Whilst scantily clad youngsters gyrated to the sounds of 'Make an impression. Use Lover's Plus condoms every time', on the local TV station, their parents spoke of AIDS in whispers. You recognised its symptoms in others – they bore the shame. People swore they did not have it but had never taken the test. Those who knew they were positive were made to stand in special lines to collect their special medicine. It was to 'de-stigmatise' the disease, said the powers that be. It was a disease that bound guilty and innocent alike, inextricably. Ntsimane, Sethunya, Lebo, bound beyond death by an unspoken secret.

Lebo, beautiful Lebo. Her skin was brown. Coffee – with lots of milk – brown. Her challenge-filled gazelle eyes gazed on men for longer than was proper. Her mouth was small, the lips full, promised passion. She had a pert nose. She wore her pure-black hair in thick, shoulder length twists, unrestrained, way before having dreads was 'making a statement'. Her hips were wide, made for childbearing. An ample, firm behind balanced below a tiny waist. It was rumoured that a blend of European and African blood flowed in her veins.

When Lebo sashayed into a room she cast a shadow on all other women. You pulled your man closer when Lebo was near. Lebo was not marriageable, the men said. She was far too beautiful – too much work. But they desired her, for she lit a blazing inferno in their loins. She stoked that fire with a half-formed smile. They chased her, unaware they were prey, pursuing predator. When she discarded them, they returned home, bedraggled, worn-out and weary. They asked for forgiveness from their real women and spoke of Lebo disparagingly – said she was easy. They said you would bear their children and the real women smiled contentedly.

Lebo seemed unwell the last time Sethunya saw her. Her skin had a greyish pallor to it. Tiny lines etched a fine grid on her dry cheeks. Her lips were shocking fuchsia pink. Her curves had been whittled away leaving boyish hips. The magnificent dreads had been lopped off. In their place was a short, wispy fine, brush cut. She had greeted Lebo. Lebo had started to say 'Dumela' back but had coughed before she got to the second syllable. It was a wracking, body-shuddering cough. It was the type of cough that extricated even the most stubborn phlegm from its sanctuary and drew blood in the process. Sethunya had wanted to make Lebo feel less embarrassed so she too had coughed. She remembered thinking: coughing must be contagious, like yawning. Since that day, four years ago, she had lived in fear. But she pressed that fear deep down into places no one could see.

Whenever Lebo's name was mentioned the fear would rise a little. When she heard that a gentleman friend of Lebo's had died, the fear changed to dejection. Then Ntsimane started to get sick. AIDS. Neither Sethunya nor Ntsimane said it out loud. It was enough to know he knew she knew and she knew he knew.

Her Ntsimane – hers and Lebo's. Sethunya rescued Ntsimane when Lebo tired of him. She, grateful to feel needed, had agreed to marry him. Sethunya loved Ntsimane so much; she knew her love would expunge Lebo forever from his heart. He loved her too, after a fashion. She was an understanding and tolerant wife. She accepted that he was weak and temptation was everywhere. Their marriage was neither very sad, nor very happy – the way a good marriage should be.

Sethunya had survived ten years of marriage by insulating herself from the sights and sounds that threatened to permeate the wall of denial she enclosed herself in. It was safer not to hear, simpler not to see. For how could she know and do nothing? Inaction was the curse of desperate women, women who knew no better. They clung to their man for it was better to be a Mrs than a Miss. It was the way of women raised to be grateful for that which they are given. Those were the women who stayed.

Sethunya prided herself on being a modern, independent, strong Motswana woman. But she stayed, shackled to Ntsimane by the need to be a good woman, immobilised by fear of a life without him. She looked the other way when Ntsimane stared too long at a pretty face. She chose not to hear him whispering flirtatious invitations into unknown ears on his phone. All she heard was the rustle of Ntsimane's trousers and shirt falling into a crumpled heap on the carpet as she opened her arms to him.

When Ntsimane said he wasn't feeling too good, her fear bubbled over, like home-made beer did when you added yeast to the brew. His health became a barometer of hers. Sethunya went to church on Wednesdays and Sundays to beseech God to forgive him. She shed tears of 'what if' and 'if only'. When her tears dried, she nursed him back to good health with the strength, devotion and love of a good wife. She nursed him till the sickness went away, till her sense of foreboding was calmed. But one day he whispered, 'Baby, I'm so tired. I need to rest.' His last words were, 'Baby I'm sorry. Please forgive me.'

News of his death spread like an autumn veld fire fanned by August trade winds. 'The virus' or 'four-letters,' they whispered. Sethunya told whoever asked that her loving husband had a rare blood disease – one for which there was no cure. Sethunya and Ntsimane were a 'we holiday abroad' kind of couple. Their kin died of exotic diseases caused by a too-refined diet. Not AIDS.

Sethunya mourned her husband's passing for twelve months, sheathed in black from head to toe as custom dictated. She wore no jewellery save her wedding band. People shied away from her; afraid she might taint them with what her husband had. They whispered and watched as they joined with her in her lonely vigil. Waiting for signs that she had it too.

Now Lebo had died. She knew it was only a matter of time before some disease unleashed itself on her and made itself known to all who saw her. The truth would out. What if she got shingles? What if it struck her in the middle of the night and left pin hole punctures on the side of her face? What if she started to lose weight, or got sores that would not heal? Every time a sore appeared on her body she examined it, every hour, to see if it was healing. She once had one that lasted two weeks… She would wake up in the middle of the night to check if it was still there.

She finally did what had to be done. She went for an HIV test. She stood in line with all the hopefuls who were a little worried and just wanting to know. It was her turn. She walked into the counselling room, perched on the edge of the chair in front of the counsellor.

He was young enough to be her son. He asked questions that made her flinch but she responded to all of them. Did she have reason to suspect she might have been infected? 'Yes.' Was she sexually active? 'No, not any more. Not for two years.' She responded to all the questions, honestly. The time for games had elapsed. As they spoke, the fluttering in her stomach was stilled and she felt calm and in control – whether it was positive or negative she was ready.

And now she held the results in her hand, in a brown envelope marked 'Private and Confidential' in big red letters. She opened the envelope and read the results. Finally, she knew. She smiled and stood up. She walked out of the testing centre. She took short steps, swayed her hips from side to side. She walked with resolve, powerfully, for there was still much for her to do and many places for her to go in this life. The words to Ntsimane's favourite hymn played over and over in her head.

'It is well. It is well. It is well with my soul.'

Election Day

Christopher Mlalazi

He suddenly stood up and punched a fist into his left palm.

'Damn!' he cursed to the empty room. Then he called out. 'Twenty!'

Twenty entered the room. He went down on his knees in front him. 'Your Excellency,' he said, his head bowed over a potbelly straining under a buttoned suit jacket.

His Excellency pointed at a sofa. 'Sit.'

Twenty sat on the edge of the sofa, and His Excellency sank back into the throne, which completely dwarfed him. Nine decades and four months old, he was now a shrivelled old man with a stooped back and teary, bloodshot eyes. He was dressed in an immaculate white safari suit, and a leopard skin cowboy hat.

He frowned, looking at Twenty's right foot. It was tapping on the richly carpeted floor. Then he smiled sweetly. 'Relax, Twenty.'

The foot immediately ceased its activity, and Twenty wiped sweat off his forehead with the back of his hand, his eyes on his knees. 'Things are bad outside Your Excellency,' he said in almost a whisper.

His Excellency jerked forward on his seat, a finger pointed at Twenty's forehead. 'Eh! Eh! Don't exaggerate!'

'I am not exaggerating – !'

'Do you know your problem, my dear comrade?' His Excellency asked, still leaning forward, his eyes on the bald patch on the crown of Twenty's head. The remaining fringe of Twenty's hair was dyed pitch-black. 'You panic very easily, just like a puppy. Woof woof behind a fence, and if you pretend to pick up a stone – it flees away with its tail between its legs!'

Twenty looked up. 'I am not panicking your Excellency,' he replied, his voice now whining, and wiped his forehead again with the back of his hand.

'Then why are you sweating like that – are you defecating?'

Twenty wiped his forehead in a sneaky manner. 'The election results are not so good, your Excellency. The ballot counting is almost finished, there is only one ballot box left uncounted, and the opposition is leading us by a very wide margin – three million votes so far, and the remaining ballot box contains less than one thousand ballot papers. We have lost. Everything is crashing down on us!'

His Excellency threw his head back and cackled in laughter. 'And you are now crapping in your pants!' He clapped his hands sharply, and cackled again. But there was no laughter in his bloodshot eyes. They glittered wetly. 'Stop being paranoid.' He wagged his finger at Twenty. 'To use your own words – it is you who is going to crash out of my elite team if you behave like an old woman who has just dreamt of her departed ancestors calling her name. Anyway,' he spread out his hands in front of his chest, palms up, his shoulders hunched. 'Why should you be frightened of the election results? You are not the leader of this country.' He paused for a moment, his eyebrows arched, his hands still spread out towards Twenty. Then he dropped them on the arms of the throne and continued. 'Let me tell you something for nothing my dear personal advisor. This is not a children's game we are playing here. This is not *ara-wuru-wuru-skoko*. It is a game of true men. Men who are larger than life. Did you read comic books when you were young?'

Twenty perked up. 'Yes I read them your Excellency – *Kid Colt, Spiderman, Superman, Tin Tin* –'

His Excellency waved his hand at him. 'No, not that shit. There is one that you have left out. My favourite.' A tiny smile flitted across his lips.

Twenty's eyes rolled to the ceiling in thought, and he looked sideways at His Excellency. 'You mean *Wonder Woman?*'

'No,' His Excellency shook his head, firmly. 'Not that prostitute.' He stood up, raised his spindly arms and flexed them, his face twisted in effort. '*The Incredible Hulk!*'

Twenty's face broke into a wide smile. 'I love him! He is my hero!'

His Excellency's teeth flashed in grim smile. 'I am the new Incredible Hulk of this continent.' He roared like Hulk, grabbed a startled Twenty and threw him to the ground. Twenty immediately rose up, fear on his face. His Excellency roared again, and threw him down for the second time. This time Twenty did not try to rise up. His Excellency strutted around the room, roaring, and flexing his thin arms. He went back to Twenty, who was still lying on the ground. Twenty cringed back in fear.

His Excellency offered him his hand, now laughing. 'Get up comrade! You look so undignified on the floor.'

Twenty took the offered hand, but used his own power to propel himself up. His Excellency sank back into the throne, and Twenty sat on the edge of the sofa, his right foot tapping again.

'That is the lesson, Twenty. Never worry – nobody can defeat the Incredible Hulk, not even with the assistance of the devil himself, or their fucking atomic bomb.'

'But, your Excellency, the election results!' said Twenty. 'It is over for us.'

An irritated frown creased His Excellency's brow. 'I told you not to bother yourself about that. Have you never heard of a soccer team leading six-nil being beaten at the very last minute without even any match-fixing?'

'I beg your pardon your Excellency, but this is not soccer –'

'Your scrotum!'

Twenty did not even blink. 'But if we lose your Excellency, what is to become of us?'

'Don't have sleepless nights over it, otherwise your wife will give it to your hungry garden boy if you are so frightened that you can't get it up for her.'

'If I may speak –'

'Shut up!'

'But your Excellency, you have not walked the streets of the cities for a very long time now. You do not know what is happening out there. As your personal advisor, I know better. I live with them…'

'Twenty – what kind of a name is that anyway? Mmh? What was your father thinking of when he gave you such a funny English name? Come to think of it, I have never heard of an Englishman with such a name either. By the way, what kind of a job was your father doing when you were born? Do you remember that far into colonialism?'

'Yes I remember,' said Twenty. 'He was employed as a garden boy – a garden man – a gardener – in the suburbs by a Mr Williams, your Excellency.'

'Then Twenty must have been a very memorable number for him to be so excited by it as to give it to his beloved son who is now personal advisor to a respected, and feared (let me not forget to mention that) Head Of State. What could have given him an erection about this number twenty? Would you know?'

'I don't know your Excellency.'

'You never even asked him?'

'No I never.'

'How could you not ask him? Maybe he was insulting you!' His Excellency smiled. 'Let me try to guess. He must have been given Twenty very sweet lemons by this Mr Williams as his salary for that month when you were born. So I think your father left other names out. He should have called you Twenty Sweet Lemons. TSL. Now let me give you some very free advice, my personal advisor. You have made a very wrong assessment of the *povo*, just like judging the sweetness of an orange by its skin, or that of a woman by the shape of her lips.'

'But this is different your Excellency...'

'My people will never desert me. Do you hear me TSL? I am their life leader if you didn't know, chosen by the ancestral spirits themselves. That is why you always hear me refer to the *povo* as my people, my country, not me their person, or their country – or even *our* country too. Simple as all that.'

Twenty spread his hands in appeal. 'But I am the one who is supposed to advise you, your Excellency. The election results –'

'Rubbish! You don't know anything about the election results! Why are you such a coward?'

'How can I not be afraid when I know very well what is waiting for us outside? The people are going to tear us to pieces.'

'They will tear your grandmother to pieces!'

'Your Excellency, I beg you to listen to me. Poverty is rife in the streets, the people are hungry, and very angry!'

His Excellency suddenly stood up, went to Twenty, and grabbed his shirt collar with both of his hands. Then he hissed into his face 'How can they not be disillusioned when you have five hundred million US dollars in your private Swiss Account, and I have one billion pounds? How can they not be angry when I have a sprawling coffee plantation in South America, limousines in every capital city in Europe, a castle in Belgium, a pleasure boat in the Indian Ocean, a private jet, a diamond mine in South Africa amongst my many international assets, and inflation here is at the ceiling? That is what you want to hear, isn't it?' He released Twenty's shirt collar, and wagged a finger at his face. 'If you run away my dear boy, you won't have far to run, because the people of this country, with the assistance of the world's robo-police of course, will hunt you down and once they catch you, you will learn not to be a dull embezzler.' He suddenly smiled, a charming smile, stooped and patted Twenty's shoulder, his face close to his. 'Calm down Twenty. Calm down. I am still around. I will take care of you, my dear boy. Haven't I done so these past years we have been working together? I even made you what you are today!'

Twenty rearranged his shirt collar. 'Yes you did, but –'

'Now get out of my sight!'

'Your Excellency!'

'I said get out!' His Excellency's hand dipped into his inside jacket pocket, and it came out holding a tiny silver pistol. Twenty jumped up from the sofa and scooted out of the room. The door closed softly.

His Excellency returned the pistol into his jacket pocket, and blew his nose at the carpet. Wiping his nose with his fingers, he went to the throne and plopped into it. He sat back, softly stroking his cleanly shaven chin in deep thought. Then he picked up a telephone on a side table, dialled, and spoke into it.

'Twenty?' He listened. 'I want to go to the back garden for some fresh air. Get the army ready, and two gunships in the air. Bring a vest for me as well. Let's meet in the kitchen right now.'

He stood up, took a walking stick that leaned against the throne and walked out of the room, balancing heavily on it.

Six members of the Presidential Guard, all armed with submachine guns, lined the corridor, three on either side. They snapped into attention when His Excellency appeared from the inner sanctum door.

He walked between them, headed towards the door of the kitchen, which was the second on the right. The third door on the left opened, and the First Lady also walked into the corridor, carrying two brown leather suitcases. At sixty years of age, she was slim-bodied, and still retained signs of her maiden beauty that had made her win a university beauty pageant at age nineteen, from where His Excellency had snapped her up.

'Modi,' His Excellency said, coming to a stop. 'Why all these bags my dear? Are you visiting somewhere? I don't remember you telling me about it?'

'Let's go and talk in there,' Modi replied in a grim voice, nodding towards the half-open door of the inner sanctum.

They stood inside it, the door closed, Modi's suitcases on either side of her.

'The jet is waiting at the airport,' she whispered in a hoarse voice. 'I have packed everything we shall need. Let us go now before they come and get us!'

'Who get us? I don't understand, dear,' His Excellency said in a calm voice.

'Have you heard the results?' Modi's eyes were opened wide in fright.

His Excellency laid his left hand, with the right one on top if it, on the head of his walking stick and regarded Modi with a slightly furrowed brow.

'The results of what, dear?'

'The election results!'

His Excellency waved a hand airily at her. 'Oh that. What of them?'

'They are winning!'

'Who is winning?'

'The opposition!'

'What are they winning?'

'The elections of course! Let us leave right now while there is still time! Oh God, I am so frightened!'

His Excellency laid a hand on her arm. 'Relax, my dear.' He pointed at a sofa. 'Sit down.'

'I am not sitting down! Let us go!'

His Excellency blinked his eyes at her. 'Go where, darling?'

'Please stop asking silly questions! You know very well what I mean. We are going to the coffee plantation in South America, or the castle in Belgium. There we shall be safe.'

'Modi, I told you to relax. Relax. Sit down. Should I order a glass of water for you?'

'I don't want it!'

His Excellency shrugged his shoulders. 'So be it.' He sat down on the arm of the sofa.

Modi stood before him. 'If you don't want to come, I am taking the children and going without you!'

His Excellency looked up at her. 'You panic easily, my dear. Everything is under control. I have just been telling that fool Twenty the very same thing. The final election results have not yet been announced, and everybody around me is already peeing in their trousers. What kind of people am I surrounded with? Surely they don't all wear nappies?'

'But the opposition is leading by a very wide margin. We have lost.'

'Modi, when I married you, I told you that I wanted a wife with nerves of steel, not a woman with the heart of a pigeon that beats a thousand times in a minute.' He stood up, went to the phone, picked it up and dialled. 'Twenty?' he said into it. 'Can you please come in?' He replaced the receiver. Then he walked to the throne and sat down. He threw his right leg over the left one, his hands laid on his lap, the fingers forming a steeple, and his eye fixed on the door meditatively. Modi's eyes were on him, her face sulking.

The door opened softly. Twenty walked in.

'Help my wife carry her bags back to her chambers.' His Excellency crisply ordered him. 'Thank you.'

Twenty looked at him. 'Your Excellency…'

'Don't make noise, you cunt! Leave, both of you!'

Twenty and Modi stood before the door of her chambers. Twenty held her suitcases in either hand.

'Can't you convince him that there is no longer any hope now?' Modi asked.

Twenty placed the suitcases on the floor and looked up at her. She was taller than him. The bald patch on his head glistened with sweat. 'I tried hard this morning ma'am, but he does not want to listen to me.'

'But you are his personal advisor!'

'Yes I am, but today he is turning a deaf ear to my advice. He is even giving me advice instead.'

'Do you think this might have affected his mind?' she whispered. 'I have never known him like this, and you know he is no longer a young man now.'

'I have never known him like this either,' Twenty said. 'He has always been a shrewd and calculating man who does not take any unnecessary risks, especially where his life is concerned, but now – I don't know. I just don't know.'

'Maybe he has become disorientated and he thinks it's his party that is leading the polls.'

'Maybe. He is behaving so strangely today. Can you imagine if we lose? I don't even want to think about it. I can already see the *povo* pouring into State House – no!' he shook his head, as if to shake off a nightmare.

'All because my husband does not want to face reality.' Modi said. 'What can I do to convince him we have to run whilst there is still time, and the airports are still open to us?'

'You know your husband's temper when he is crossed ma'am,' Twenty said. 'A few minutes back he nearly shot me.'

Tears sprang into Modi's eyes. She opened the bedroom door, took the suitcases and went inside. The door closed as Twenty walked away from it along the corridor.

His Excellency, sitting on the throne, picked up the phone from the side table and dialled.

'Twenty? Is the vote-counting finished? Good. I don't want to hear the final results. Tell Amon to announce them to the people on the national electronic media. In the meantime, I will be in the bathroom preparing myself for the people, since, to use your words, they now want my blood.' He banged the phone down. There was a determined look on his old face. He stood up from the throne, took his walking stick, and walked towards the door, his body erect.

Modi sat on the bed in her bedroom, her eyes fixed on a big-screen colour television on a table before her. On it Amon, the National Vote Director, stood behind a podium in the vote-counting room. A battery of TV cameras and microphones were arrayed before him. In his hand he held a single sheet of paper. He cleared his throat, and spoke.

'Ladies and gentlemen, good evening. Now for the moment we have all been waiting for. The final results of the vote-counting.' Modi sighed deeply. Her heart was pounding in her chest. 'Ladies and gentlemen, the impossible has happened tonight. I am sure the opposition are already celebrating, wherever they are right now, and their leader is preparing to go to State House.'

Modi placed her right hand over her heart. It was now thudding.

'The opposition has done the impossible!'

Modi bit her lower lip, and the TV screen swam as tears filled her eyes.

'They have lost the election, when at one time they were leading by three million votes and there was only one ballot box left uncounted. Thank you, ladies and gentleman.'

Modi toppled back on the bed in a faint.

The TV droned on. 'These were very free and fair elections, so the international observers have declared...'

Double Shame

Beatrice Fri Bime

Saint Theresa's Cathedral of Kumbo in Nso Bui Division was the venue of the wedding, which was the only exciting activity taking place on that second Saturday of August in the year of our Lord nineteen hundred and ninety-nine. The wedding bells, like the couple taking their vows, had come from America. The expectations of the wedding were high.

The parents of the couple were well-known retired civil servants who were now enjoying their golden years between the village, the Mankon cosmopolitan town of Bamenda and visiting their children in the various American and European towns where they were found. The idea to do the wedding in their hometown had been the decision of the girl's parents and not that of the couple being married. The parents thought it was a good idea to show off in the town, while at the same time feed the villagers. The young couple would have preferred to take their vows in the USA, where most of their friends could attend. As it was, they had bowed to their parents wishes and ended up with more of their parents' friends than theirs.

The central aisle of the cathedral was lined with a disposable red carpet and the walls and stands were decorated with flowers imported from America. If it rained, everything would be ruined. People would come into the cathedral with muddy feet. So, for that day, ushers and usherettes advised people to go into the church through the side doors. The wedding was to be a mixture of indigenous and Western celebration. Some of the songs would be in the vernacular while some would be in English. But the special offertory procession was going to be all in the dialect. After the offertory, where individuals walked up to the basket nearest to their seats and put their offerings, the couple, family and friends were to be led into church by members of the choir. The two who led the couple would be dressed in traditional loin cloths, tied round the waist like a sarong and adorned with heavy beads. Holding cutlasses, they would dance forward to the rhythm of the song, run ahead and come back brandishing the cutlasses in the air, then striking them together to make a loud, clanking sound. For anyone seeing the performance for the first time, it resembled a war dance. The procedure was repeated over and over as the procession walked at a solemn pace to the beat of the music. The couple always carry the wine and the chalice, and in some Roman Catholic churches that was the only day in their lives when they were given that privilege. The family carries anything from goats and chickens, to raw foodstuff and drinks. During this particular wedding, the gifts were as extravagant as was expected. The priest came up to personally receive the offerings. Reluctant goats were dragged into church protesting with loud *meh-mehs,* while the cocks crowed and flapped their wings as they were lifted up for show. At such occasions, most married couples renewed their vows or wondered if they could have done theirs in the same way.

Mr Menjo watched the bride walk down the aisle looking pretty and happy. He nudged his wife of thirty years and smiled at her, then whispered, 'If we had to do it again, I think we could do it like this – what do you think?'

'Okay,' Mrs Menjo answered, feeling very happy that her husband never imagined that he could have chosen anyone else.

'Our Lem would make a prettier bride on her wedding day,' Mr Menjo said.

'I bet.' His wife smiled at him, indulging her husband, who loved their first daughter to distraction. Sometimes the plans Mr Menjo had for his beautiful daughter were distracting. There were times when Mrs Menjo thought that her husband had started planning their daughter's wedding before the poor child was two. It never occurred to him that anything could spoil all those plans.

On Sundays, while other parents relaxed, Mr Menjo would gather little girls who had come to play with their daughter and say proudly to them: 'You, you will be a flower girl for my Lem when she is getting married. You will be dressed in pink and all the other little bridesmaids will be dressed just so…' Mr Menjo would use his hands to demonstrate the frilly gowns he dreamed the bridesmaids of his daughter would be wearing. Mr Menjo dreamed of his daughter's wedding and planned everything down to the smallest detail. Lemjo was not yet eighteen and had no suitors yet, but he never considered the possibility that something could ruin his plans. He was the grandson of a Catholic catechist. His father had been a catechist and Catholic schoolteacher. Their family was well known and respected in the community. They had been brought up good practising Catholics. He was now a retired lawyer. His six children had taken after him. He doted on all of them, but no one needed to be told that his first daughter was the centre of his heart.

Three years later, Lemfon's parents felt ashamed. They had sent her to a good mission school. They had brought her up the best way they could. So how could she shame them like this? Not only had she got pregnant, she was cohabiting with the author of the pregnancy. Their daughter and this man had gone and signed a paper in court without bothering to consult them or performing any of the traditional rites.

Lemfon, their beautiful daughter, that calm and quiet child of theirs, barely eighteen, already had a fiancé. The fiancé was a tribe's boy from a good family. Everything had been arranged between the parents and Lemfon had raised no objections. How could she do this to them? Mr Menjo blamed his wife as most men do when a child misbehaves. Mrs Menjo kept her hurt bottled inside and wondered what she would do if she ever again saw that child of hers whom her husband had banned from stepping foot in their compound.

The months went by and the hurt and humiliation dimmed, then Lemfon sent a message that she had given birth to a baby girl and would be happy if her parents sent a name for the baby. After much thought, Mr Menjo named the baby Sevidzem which means 'Accept-all'. Mrs Menjo missed her daughter and she wanted to go and visit her grandaughter. After many arguments and much pleading, Mr Menjo gave her permission to do so.

With excitement and a high sense of anticipation, she took a week to prepare for the journey. She took some cobs of corn, husked them and ground the grains into flour. She shelled a bag of beans, cut some avocado pears and oranges. Mr Menjo plucked some kola nuts from the kola nut tree standing in the middle of the compound and tied them together. He went to his chicken pen, took time to look at the cocks, chose a huge bird and put it in a latticed basket woven with dry outer bamboo ropes and decorated with a thick white mark running across the side of the basket.

Mrs Menjo was to travel by public transport, because in spite of the fact that he had accepted that she could go, Mr Menjo had vehemently said he was not going to send any of his cars to take her on the journey. She boarded the bus after paying for excess luggage.

The Hiace bus that was meant for twelve people now seated eighteen. It rumbled on the dusty road, over bumps and turns. The police stopped them at Melim, a few kilometres from Kumbo Nso', then gendarmes stopped them at Sob and Jakiri, towns barely three kilometres apart, and again at Ndop in the division next to Bui. At Bambui the gendarmes said someone's identity card had expired and the bus was kept there for over thirty minutes because the person refused to give the bribe the policeman asked for. The journey, which would have taken ninety minutes had the road been tarred, normally took two and a half hours. Now, four hours later with all the stops and delays, it was finally on the tarred portion of the road at Nkwen, the satellite town at the entrance to the city of Bamenda… and yet another policeman lifted his hand and blew his whistle. Not another bloody police check, every passenger sighed.

Just as the policeman was disembarking, having inspected the vehicle's documentation and the passengers' identity cards, the cock crowed and flapped its wings inside the basket.

'Who has the fowl?' he demanded.

'Na me, sar,' Mrs Menjo said in a voice both humble and full of impatience.

'Whose sai books for the fowl?'

The pot-bellied policeman wanted the bird's health certificate.

'I no bi know say fowl get to get book, sar.'

'If the fowl has no documents then I'm sorry, the fowl cannot be allowed into town.'

The policeman picked up the basket. Walking with a slight limp, he took it out of the bus and placed it on to the gravel verge. Mrs Menjo could hardly believe what was happening, and so close to her destination as well. But she was so tired, thirsty, dusty and eager to reach her destination, she said that if the cock was all that was keeping them, then they should leave the cock and go.

The policeman nodded and waved them on.

At the bus terminal, all the luggage was brought down from the top of the bus. In her excitement to see her daughter, Mrs Menjo had overlooked how inconvenient the quantity of foodstuffs she had brought would be to carry. With no idea of the distance involved, she promised to pay a wheelbarrow pusher a thousand francs an hour to push her things to her daughter's, then she asked an agent of the bus company if he could direct her to the house of a Nso man. The agent was used to such enquiries from passengers. He told her that he also was from Nso, and could direct her if he knew who she was looking for.

'I di look for my pickin weh e name nah Lemfon.'

'Mammy, weti your pickin dei do? You know whose sai e die work?'

'No. Ei marry some man.'

Mrs Menjo listened to herself and could not believe it. Here she was, a former primary school teacher who ate boys like this for breakfast, talking as if she was some uneducated village woman because of this stupid child. She did not even know what her daughter's husband's name was, so she started asking everyone, describing her daughter until someone finally led her to someone who knew where she lived.

Some time later, Mrs Menjo found herself being led down a footpath towards a a house built with mud bricks and roofed with corrugated iron sheets. She stopped and said to the young man who was helping her, 'I am not sure you know the daughter I am looking for. She cannot be living in such a place. Where are you taking me to?'

'Madam,' he answered, 'if we reach no bi yar pickin no bi you fit leavam?'

Her heart beating very loudly, she suddenly realised that the young woman in the yard hanging diapers on the line was Lemfon! Mrs Menjo did not know whether to cry, or to laugh hysterically. She had to be in a very bad dream. This could not be happening to her, or to her Lem. Before she could decide what to do, her daughter turned her head, saw her, and rushed into her arms.

They hugged each other in tears. Lemfon heated water for her mother and took the water to a bathroom that was shared by other tenants. Mrs Menjo quietly took a bath to wash off the dust. She could not remember the last time she had had to do so in such conditions. Afterwards, she tenderly held her grandchild in her arms. The baby was so beautiful. Mrs Menjo remembered the time she first held Lemfon in her arms in the St Elizabeth's General Hospital at Shisong.

'How was your trip?' Lemfon asked.

'Tiring, and I had the worst experience just as we entered town. The cock your father sent to you was taken by a policeman.'

'You mean Papa actually sent me a cock, Mama? Has he forgiven me?'

'I should think so. A baby usually bridges any rift.'

'So I can bring my husband home and introduce him to you people?'

'Of course, if you want to be properly married. Why did you decide to rush into marriage, my daughter? Your father and I had so many plans for you.'

'Wait until you meet my husband, Mama, you will like him.'

'Of course, you know that your father always dreamed of walking you down the aisle to your husband.'

'He can still do that,' Lemfon answered.

'We always assumed you would complete your education before getting married. Dan's parents knew that and accepted it.'

At this mention of the former suitor, mother and daughter looked at each other and silently decided not to bring up the topic again.

'Mama, I love my husband,' Lemfon said, 'I hope you will like him when you meet him. Please give him a chance.'

'I can't promise anything. You know, if your father was not too embarrassed, he would have had him locked up, don't you?'

'Thank God he didn't, because I would have chosen him over Papa. Mama, I love my husband. He is a nice man.'

'You keep talking about love, but what do you know about it at your age?'

'Enough to know I am happy with him.'

'Living like this?'

'Mama, please,' Lemfon said, 'he will progress in his job. I hope we will be as happy as you and Papa are. Wish me that.'

'Every parent's wish is to see their children happy. I wish that and more for you.'

The sun was setting. Mrs Menjo was contentedly holding her granddaughter and singing lullabies to her.

'*Oh oh la dze ton. Oh oh la dze ton. Macti Mamie wii for kwa, oh oh la la oh la oh.*'

'*Oh oh la dze ton. Oh oh la dze ton. Macti Mamie wii for kwa, oh oh la la oh la oh.*'

The baby was sound asleep but Mrs Menjo was still holding her on her lap, not wanting to put her in her cot. A cock crowed and she looked up. A policeman was walking towards the house. He was carrying a basket. Mrs Menjo blinked, and then blinked again.

That was her basket, that was the policeman who had taken her fowl. She recognised the white line on the side of her basket and the policeman's slight limp.

What was he doing, coming this way?

He walked right up to the house, and then Lemfon came out to meet him. Mrs Menjo's head was throbbing. This could not be happening.

'Please Lord, let this not be my son-in-law,' she prayed. But who else would her daughter be welcoming with an embrace?

As if in a dream, Mrs Menjo heard him say, 'Darling, I brought you a chicken.'

'Oh that's wonderful, because my mother is here.'

The policeman turned to be introduced and looked into the eyes of the woman whose chicken he had taken. They stared at each other and he let the basket drop to the ground.

Mrs Menjo recovered first.

'So you are the young man who stole my daughter's heart?' she said quite calmly.

Mrs Menjo had gone to Bamenda prepared to stay for a minimum of a month, as required by tradition. So, when she returned within a week, there was a stir. Women friends came to visit and teased her: 'Even at this age you could not bear to be away from your husband for too long?'

Mrs Menjo replied, 'And give some young woman the opportunity to lure him away from me? No way!'

However, when they asked, 'How is the baby?'

'Fine.' Mrs Menjo replied with a smile. 'She looks so much like Lemfon that I almost imagined I was holding my own daughter again.'

'And Lemfon?'

'Fine.' Mrs Menjo would reply with a sad smile.

'And the baby's father?'

'They are all fine. Only, my daughter is married to a thief.'

Over the Garden Wall

Linda Cracknell

His lips sent beads of the recent rain quivering down the waxy red curve of the frangipani petal. The sun had reclaimed the sky again, crashing black shadows onto the ground, and returning colours to primary. But drips still beat onto the lower foliage of the garden, flicking leaves up and down like piano keys with no apparent player. It was the first time that the frangipani bush had flowered, and he lingered over it with his face and fingers and his inhalations, soaking in the sense that it was only there because of him, because he had planted and nurtured it. Now he would be the one to enjoy it.

Someone from home had written to congratulate him on his garden 'retreat'. Outrage advanced on him in the hours after reading the letter. As if he was the sort of man to retreat. He had written back straight away, saying quite to the contrary, he considered his garden an 'attack'. Hadn't his campaign involved taking possession of the land, a blitz on the scrambling native bush, a colonisation of the fragrant and the flamboyant? And wasn't he right now safeguarding his territory, securing its borders?

He had set a flame to the letter with its impertinent – 'So sorry to hear'.

His world was complete. Mangoes fell, ready sliced onto his plate; prawns, by the bucketful. There was always a cold beer to cool his throat as he stared from his bar terrace across the Indian Ocean. The heavy curve of a young shark's backbone over the back of a bicycle would soon be straightened as he carried it to his kitchen. He could drive to another beach if he wanted to, or perhaps to the bar on the west, where the sunsets were better.

Everywhere he went, people straightened their backs in the fields or turned mid-purchase in the market, and raised a hand in the air for him. And they called out his name – children and adults. He couldn't hear them because the air-conditioning didn't work properly unless the car windows were shut. But he saw his name in the shape of their lips. It made him rise upright in his seat. Even though they gave it freely, he was determined to deserve their respect – the man who, with the barest soil on this hard white coral rock of an island, had made frangipani and bougainvillaea blossom, and filled the night air with the scent of ylang-ylang.

He relished the world he had created as he drew on his cigar underneath the stars and the moon, listening to the dark crash of the waves. The night air was full of the trilling creatures he had attracted. He didn't know whether the disembodied sounds were made by birds, insects, frogs maybe. And he didn't want to see, in case they were ugly scuttling things that would make him want to pull his bare feet away.

Even during the day much of his time was spent on the terrace with a beer in one hand, gazing out across his own private lagoon, with his garden hooting and trilling behind him. He played in whispers with the similar sound of the words 'lagoon' and 'saloon'. He had both here, two in one, he joked to himself. He did that – played with words, plaited and unravelled them. Recently, 'stronghold' and 'stranglehold' had come into his head together – unrelated, and yet so similar in sound. A lifetime of crossword puzzles must have done that to him. The mind sparring with itself.

About a mile out, he could see waves breaking over the reef – he could hear them, in fact. Boats would come edging through the shallows, working their way a few miles south to the break where an underwater cliff sheered downwards and they could escape, to fish the deeper sea. At first he had felt that the turquoise water of the lagoon belonged to him. He had wanted the boats to stay out. The dhows and poled canoes, and rickety dug-outs with their outriggers had the whole of the purple-blue sea beyond the reef as their realm. He wasn't going to take that from them.

But as time went on he had noticed that the boats scudding along the lagoon didn't interrupt the stark whiteness of his coral beach by coming ashore. The men's heads turned towards him, and their hands rose. That was all. In the early days he had stood, the captain on his bridge, as they went past. But not now. He just let them pass.

Anyone who looked into his garden could see that life was good because he made it so. After a lifetime of postings, and stations here and there, of being exposed to this and that danger, he'd made himself secure. He'd trucked in dark rich soil from the mainland to embed his roots, and imported dried blood and bone meal from Europe. Now he was enclosed by a rising tanglewood of green.

When he drove through the village at night, he saw folk clustered in the lamplight and shadows, and he smelt roasting fish. There was laughter and music from a tinny radio, but no electricity, and he saw that they used the most basic of implements. With his garden, he had shown them what was possible, how they didn't need to live on top of each other in huts full of charcoal smoke, and stand in their doorways each dawn to sweep at the hard coral they had chosen to support their lives.

As the garden's riches had grown, it had drawn in intruders. More sweet almonds must hit the ground than remained under the tree in the morning, and it wasn't just the fruit bats to blame. The rustle and thump behind him at dusk was surely someone raiding the mango tree. Paths with an ancient, bare-foot quality began to appear. The white sandy trails worn amongst the trees reminded him of through-routes across wasteland, between housing estates, in his long lost past. And he didn't want to be reminded of the trickle of sweat down his back. Running through the scrub from the sound of pursuing footsteps. The Barr Boys next door and his mother reminding him, 'we're polite to neighbours, aren't we, now?'

No one wanted thieves in their garden.

There were dogs too. He heard them at night, roaming and howling as a pack. And he heard the squeals of their victims. The dogs scavenged for waste at the back doors of hotels, collectively wolfish. (How similar 'dog' was to 'god', he noticed. And yet gods were singular. A 'pack of gods' was unthinkable.) He didn't want dogs in his garden either.

The disappearing fruit and the dogs hadn't galvanised him though, on reflection. It was the trouble that started things. Gangs of young men, fired up with – what? Hunger? He shook his head, doubted it. (He made a mental note at the same time though, of the similar sound of 'hunger' and 'anger'.) Drugs perhaps. Or just fired up by being young men. They came with *pangas* and slashed at people and property. The Italian hotel-owner a few miles down the coast had to be helicoptered out with his injuries. Word was it was an orchestrated attack, outsiders, probably from the mainland.

It was true that the thick, rich foliage he had created around himself provided perfect cover for someone to creep up on him. In the middle of the night, he would sometimes raise his head from the pillow at a sound penetrating the jungle of his dreams. He didn't even open his eyes, and slumped back down to resume sleep as soon as he was reassured. But he began to feel the need for clearer definition where the garden bordered the road to the village – something between the green and the white. And he would get an *askari* too, to act sentry for him at the entrance, an *askari* with a dog.

He dallied with the idea of a thorn hedge – both burglar-proof and beautiful. Like a hostile hedge of holly that he would have thought of to surround the Surrey garden with its roses and striped lawns. The garden he had worked so hard to out-do here. The hedge would be impregnable, ten feet high, five feet in diameter, a strong single species to provide privacy and protection. Our passion for privacy, he thought, that's what makes us different from the people here.

But his plan remained a plan.

The story of the Italian-run hotel reached the British newspapers and she had written saying, 'You told me it was completely safe there – a paradise.' Not long afterwards she wrote again saying how beautiful the azaleas were that spring and how the Fosters had a new spaniel pup, and that she would stay there after all for the summer. And then the final letter saying, 'There's someone else.'

He tripped as he broke through the deep shade of the garden, reading the letter. Sunlight on the terrace flashed off the white page and blinded him for a moment. The jolt fizzed up his heartbeat.

Then he had decided. A hedge would take time to grow. Whereas a wall could materialise quickly.

'Mattress?'

'Eheh.'

'Fridge?'

'Eheh.'

'TV?'

'Eheh.'

Hassan met Idi's grunts of assent with incredulity. Was it possible that a boy from his own village would get all these riches? He laughed, slapping his hand against the breeze-block wall that Idi sat astride.

'So he pays you in dollars?'

'He will.'

Hassan grew tall. 'I can help you.'

'It's a job for one. That's what he said.'

'You could ask him for me, brother. You know him – he's your friend.'

'He's my boss. Not my friend.'

'It's the same.'

'I've nearly finished anyway.'

Idi swung onto the ladder, and climbed down onto the lane that led to the village. He stood back and admired his handiwork – the regular rows of blocks fixed together one on top of the other with cement which set fast in the sun. Many people had come to watch at first. Now the wall stretched on three sides of the man's ground. The fourth side needed no wall, it was delineated by the hard white slab of the beach which was regularly patrolled.

'Like New York,' he said to Hassan. 'Wall Street.' And they both laughed, thinking of magazine pictures someone at school had shown them of white men perched high on the towering structure of the Empire State Building. They had presumably got so high by piling block upon block in just the same way.

Hassan lay back in his barrow of coconuts, and cracked one open with a blow of his *panga*. He drank and then handed it to Idi. He was taking coconuts to the village to sell for a couple of shillings each. But he was never going to get a mattress, let alone a TV or fridge by selling coconuts.

The next day as Hassan passed the wall, Idi called down to him: 'There's dollars for you too.'

'Yeah?' Hassan dropped the arms of his wooden barrow.

'He needs glass.'

'Glass?'

'Drinking glasses, soda bottles, whisky, whatever.'

Hassan leant against his barrow, with folded arms. 'Where would I get glass?'

'You take that,' Idi pointed at the barrow. 'Around the hotels. It's perfect for collecting glass.'

'You expect me to pay the deposit?'

'Tt,' Idi shook his head.

'To steal them?'

'Collect the broken ones.'

'He wants broken glass?' Hassan and Idi stared at each other for some time. 'You're mad brother. Why?'

Idi pointed up at the top of the wall separating the bumpy lane from the rich green trees beyond. His finger traced a range of high spiky mountains along the ridge of it.

When Idi heard a rattle coming along the coral-rag lane the next day, he began to mix cement. The orchestra grew louder as it passed through the scrub along the side of the wall that led to the beach. Idi could see from his perch on the wall how half Hassan's barrow was filled with the usual glossy green cases of coconuts, but the other half was flashing and sparkling in the sun.

'How's it going?' Hassan called up at Idi who was smearing the top of the wall with a thick dollop of cement.

'Cool.'

'Now what, brother?'

Idi pointed at the glass in the barrow and beckoned. 'Come on, give them here.'

Hassan picked at random the red metal cap and green neck of a Johnnie Walker bottle. He held it upside-down, as if it were a ceremonial sword. A sharp shard of pointed glass rose from one side of the neck, ending in a jagged point. He saw the sun fill it, swirl around inside the neck, glint on the barbed peak.

'Quick, man, it's setting.' Idi beckoned again.

'Take care,' said Hassan.

'Get real.' Idi planted the bottle top firmly in the wet cement, its lethal point spearing upwards. 'Another. Hurry.'

Hassan selected one at a time and passed them up – the thick knobbly glass of deposit-only soda bottles that he had always thought impossible to break; clear spirit bottles; broken drinking glasses with stems. He'd seen tourists drinking from them, mixing the juice of fruits with spirits. They got pinker and laughed more, and then the girls slipped off, hand-in-hand with men, onto the night-beach.

He watched silently as Idi worked his way along the wall that enclosed the birdful, fruitful, sweet-smelling garden.

He was still laughing when Idi told him to move the ladder along the wall, and descended to join him. 'We need more glass.'

Hassan pointed at the sparkling crest of the wall. It made him think of the boys in town who competed to have the brightest and longest fringes on the back of their bicycle saddles, so as to be the coolest. He'd also heard of cooks at the hotels who were told to put leaves, and even flowers, on the plates of tourist food, with no expectation that they would be eaten.

He finally squeezed out: 'He pays you to make this?'

'Eheh.'

'Why?'

'You said you wanted dollars too,' said Idi. 'Why didn't you bring a full barrow?'

'But what does he want it for?'

81

Idi looked at the wall. 'He's made a beautiful place.'

'I remember,' said Hassan. 'But now no one sees it. Just the ornament.'

'Like you said. It's sharp.'

Hassan thought for a moment and looked up at the line of rising sharks' teeth. 'Does he keep animals? Monkeys perhaps, that he wants to eat, that mustn't escape?'

'No.'

'There must be something in there. Something that can climb so high.'

'Get more glass,' said Idi. 'We have the whole wall to do, beginning to end.'

The barrow changed its tune. It no longer rumbled past the wall each day with its rolling ripe coconuts, but approached with a distinctive jingle and chatter of glass that stopped somewhere along the foot of the wall, wherever Idi was with the cement.

Hassan got to know all the hotels on that part of the island, and went further and further to collect their breakages. Some of them had got wise to the demand and started to make a charge. And so he had become a businessman, calculating shillings against the dollars he would get at the end of the job, making trips later in the day for coconuts which would pay for the glass. He sent small boys for any shimmering scraps they could find in the sand at the edges of the hotel properties.

The glass nicked his fingers and sometimes it arrived at the wall sprinkled with blood. He bought gloves in the market. And he bought a pair of shades from someone he knew in town. They were scratched, but they looked cool. New York, New York, where all the chicks were, and dollars came from, and he supposed the man behind the wall, who he had never actually spoken to.

At nights, lolling on the *baraza*, the gathered boys would talk about their futures. Idi and Hassan bragged about the refrigerators that Eddie in town was going to fetch them from Dubai. One each, and an extra one for Idi's cousin. They'd seen photographs. They repeated the names of the special properties – freezer compartments, and thermostats, and ice-cube makers. The other boys speculated on where they would gather glass the next day to sell on for shillings to Hassan the glass-entrepreneur.

'This one,' Hassan threw an arm over Idi's shoulder. 'He's going to be richest. He has dollars for *two* refrigerators.'

'Not yet,' said Idi.

'No?' Hassan winked at the other boys in the half-light.

He lay there with the calculator in his hand. He would get a wife, a mattress, a fridge and a TV. In that order. Or maybe he would need the mattress before the wife. That was what he liked to talk about with the boys on the *baraza*, or think about as he drifted towards sleep.

Other conversation washed over him – the local politics that the boys teased apart; or the declining tuna catch and how it was linked to dynamite fishermen from the mainland who encroached on their patch and were wrecking the reef for the next generation; that low-slung car with the shaded windows that had appeared briefly and then flashed south again, and who it might belong to.

When the boys occasionally ran dry of subjects, the wall would sometimes resurface. But Hassan no longer thought much about why the man wanted it, the only wall on the whole island without rooms attached to it for people to shelter in.

'Wives,' one of the boys said. 'He has to stop them from running away.'

'Why do they run?' Another boy, laughing.

'Because he's too ugly.'

'Not rich enough.'

'Tt.' Heads were shaken in disbelief. They had never seen a single wife going in or out.

A new voice rose up in the dark – a boy visiting from the next village. 'What's it he's keeping *out?*' His laugh barked into the night. But Hassan barely heard the jabbering argument that followed.

Hassan and Idi worked their way around the enclosure, planting the glass. The fourth side was the beach, and remained open. Idi could see the man watching over it from his elevated terrace. The boys completed one side of the wall from beach to lane, then the other side. Then they started the last stretch along the lane itself. There was only one small section that they didn't decorate with glass – the big metal door at the entrance. The door had a tiny little slot that an *askari* peered through. But he barely grunted at them, never came out or chatted. He wore a uniform and had a kiosk in there, Idi said. He could see from the top of the wall. People said he came from the mainland, an ex-policeman.

'Sharp teeth,' said Hassan. 'They have sharper teeth on the mainland. Like the wall.'

With Hassan's glass foraging, and Idi's cementing, they were approaching the end of the job, the corner where the lane met with the wall coming up from the beach. The final barrow of glass chinkled in, and Idi filled the last gap with the pointed shard of a 7-Up bottle, still with a clean white logo on its side. Idi climbed down the ladder, and he and Hassan whooped and slapped hands.

'Now, rich-man brother,' said Hassan. 'You can give me my share of the dollars, right?'

'You'll get them. Sure,' said Idi.

The man was in the habit of walking his garden each day, to see that all was under control, prowling into the corners, inspecting, asserting his rule. Since the growth of the wall, there was less and less need to look for intruders over his shoulder, and no need to greet passers-by. The defences were complete and there was no one to see him. He was finally secure and singular.

He had woken that morning with a flutter of anticipation. What would he find flowering? He went out after the rain, closed his eyes and breathed in the garden's scents. As he walked the bounds, he found himself pausing to lay his cheek against the smooth cool flesh of a banana leaf, cup its purple bud between his hands. He even put his lips to the first petals of the frangipani bush. A kiss, almost.

He took a pair of secateurs with him, and a notebook and pencil to write instructions for the boy when he came in – what should be chopped or tidied, or brought into the house for a vase. He checked the shape of the breadfruit tree; noted where a little tying-in would help the passion fruit vine to fan out further; decided which fruit to gather. 'Hibiscus' he whispered to himself as he wrote. 'Prune. Use shears.' The words hissed out like a leaking hose in an English summer garden. Precious and slow. '*Billbergia nutans*. Divide,' he wrote. He looked at the last word. How close it was to 'divine'. This brought a satisfying feeling.

But there was still some business to complete. The wall-boy had worked well, and had found glass for the top of it from somewhere. He had finished in good time, as he had promised, for his bonus. Now he deserved payment. The man would go to the safe as soon as the boy presented himself at the gate.

The ladder remained on the outside of the wall. As the final stretch of glass defence was now complete, he asked the *askari* to go out to the lane and retrieve the ladder from the boy. He had intended for it to be stored under lock and key at the entrance kiosk. But as he was studying a bougainvillaea newly planted against the wall, the *askari* approached, head down and sullen, lugging the ladder behind him.

At the same time, the man became aware of noise coming from the other side of the wall. This was nothing new. Usually it was people passing, and the noise passed with them. But he could hear slaps, and tinkles of glass. More than anything though, he could hear voices. They rose and fell, raw and throaty, too uninhibited to be harmless. And they didn't move on. He imagined a pack of men trying to burrow under the wall like wild dogs. He knew the diamond hardness of the coral rag, knew that this would be impossible, but still he pictured their raw scrabbling paws, snouts white with sand, drilling deep.

He pointed the *askari* to where he wanted the ladder against the wall, and then dismissed him, back to the kiosk. He was a heavy man, some had even dared to suggest he was short, and he was unused to stairs. He dragged himself up the ladder, a step at a time, until he was eye-level with his sparkling battlements. His head burst suddenly out of the variegated shade into bright sunlight. The shock of harsh white light tipped his balance momentarily. Because of the dazzle, he didn't immediately see the gaggle of boys in celebratory mood. Nor did they at first notice him.

As his vision clarified, he saw the handcart, full of coconuts. He flinched as a *panga* came down with a long slow swing, thwacking on the skull-like fruit. He recognised the wall-boy he had employed. But he had insisted that the boy worked alone, and he'd never seen anyone else up on the wall. So who were all these others who lolled bare-chested and insolent, piratical in dark glasses? Each took a swig from the coconut, the backs of their hands swiping at their mouths afterwards. What was their intention – were they planning a raid and was this their pre-battle ritual?

He watched, made invisible by his stillness, wary of upsetting the balance of the ladder. His throat was hot, his legs beginning to tremble at being too high off the ground, his hands sweating on the ladder poles. He waited for signs of hostility, for weapons, or salutes or signals of aggression – for the gang to muster.

But the coconut passed between them with only laughter and a teasing kind of pushing and pulling at each other. A generosity of arms hung loosely around shoulders. Talk flicked up and down amongst them; a percussion of hand slaps. He watched.

And as he watched, a dam shoring up a reservoir of memory gave way. A tide of laughter and chinking glasses. Bubbles of champagne snickering up his nose. A garden party on a lawn. She turned to smile at him. When she came over, he let her pick a strawberry seed from his lip before she linked his arm and they joined a new circle of friends and neighbours.

The ladder was buffeted by the current. He clung tighter to it.

The boys looked up at a rustling in the palm fronds and saw the pink face above the wall, as if it was impaled on a shard of glass, or as if the man was trying to escape from his own enclosure. Hassan saw something on the face, almost like embarrassment, like someone being caught doing something they were not supposed to do. A silence fell.

'Take him a coconut,' Idi hissed at Hassan. 'It's my boss.'

Hassan took up his *panga* again and thwacked open a young fruit. He cut into it a drinking-sized hole and lifted it up the wall, towards the man. 'You're welcome,' he said.

But without the ladder, Hassan was unable to reach high enough and the man's hands were too low on the other side of the wall.

'Take it,' said Hassan, grinning up at the pink confused face, his arm at full stretch. And he saw the man lumber a little against the wall, as if he might be trying to raise himself far enough to lean over. But he stayed where he was, at the same height.

'We're drinking to your wall,' said Hassan. 'It's finished.'

The man gave a lop-sided grin or grimace and it looked for a moment as if he would say something.

Taking his opportunity for the question he had almost forgotten, Hassan asked, 'What is it for? The wall – the glass.'

There was a moment of hesitation, a sideways glance. Hassan turned to see smirks smearing one or two of the faces behind him. And when he looked back, he thought perhaps he understood the flicker of an answer crossing the man's face.

He was sweating in the sun, and pressured by the height. He looked back over his shoulder as if for the reassurance of familiar territory, but the swaying movement of foliage behind him only cast his stomach like a buoy on waves. Half a dozen eager faces were peering at him. And they had asked him a question.

'It's...' he muttered. ' It's to...'

The boy with the coconut was smiling up at him, his arm outstretched. There was no malice in the face, but he could see that the smile was faltering, becoming less sure. It reminded him of being with his aunt. He had been sent away to stay with her for the holidays and she was pushing chocolate milk-shake towards him in a posh London café. It was a treat and he knew he couldn't tell her that he felt sick. That would be rude. Instead he had vomited a brown sludge across the white tablecloth.

He hazarded a further step on the ladder, to get the height to reach over for it – the sweet juice offered to him by the smiling boy. But as his foot faltered onto the step, he felt the ladder wobble beneath him on the uneven ground, felt the need to descend to where he felt comfortable, to the soil and his dense green cover. He slipped backwards a little, arms and legs gecko-spread. The ladder felt too steep, as if it might peel back. There was no one there to hold it. Not on his side of the wall.

He saw the ladder arms lift and come towards him. A heart-throb-blinding stab of fear sent his hand forward to grab at something solid. He found purchase. His hand closed on the high sharp spear of a smashed Fanta bottle. The peak of his creation.

Blood sprang crimson bright, spurted in an arc over the spangled glass battlements and spattered onto the white ground beyond. A deep cut and gush reeled him backwards, so that he lost sight of the boys with their flickering grins, splashed back amongst the shiny leaves of his beautiful garden – his lagoon, saloon, the turquoise world of sea and sky that he now saw through sun-speckled foliage.

As his rich arterial blood flowed, he barely heard the chorus of cries led by Idi, 'Sir, sir,' as the boys found themselves truly walled out. He didn't hear footsteps running to the entrance, the battering against the metal gate and the appeals to the *askari* for his slow help.

His blood seeped in beads back into the earth and collected in pools on the glossy green leaves of the breadfruit tree that he had pulled down with him.

Losing Jacarandas

Hester Ross

Jacaranda flowers.

From the British Hospital, the town stretches out below her – she has photographed it many times – the old colonial houses and even some of the red brick 'independence' bungalows like her own are hidden under their canopy of trees. Tall silver blue gums – left and grown too tall for easy harvesting – have strayed from the plantation on the side of the plateau down into the edges of the municipality. But mostly the trees are dark and slow growing: African hardwoods like Mbawa and Kachere and the generous old Mangoes. Here and there, Jacarandas stand out like a rash in the afternoon heat: their blue frenzy mocking the deliberate slowness of the exhausted municipality beneath. Masongola town can barely breath the hot dry air of the October day. It takes its rest in this afternoon hour: chewing its sugar canes in the cool of the big Mango trees; propping up its bicycles and its head-bundles of wood against the broad trunks; closing its eyes and praying for the coming rain. And everywhere, the roads – like the broken tarmac drive which twists up to this place – are running blue with Jacaranda flowers. These trees are exotic to sub-Saharan Africa: aliens planted once in diplomatic gardens and spreading their seed in the red African clay. Any botanist will be pleased to tell you that – and there is no shortage of botanists in the university town.

Her husband is one of them: he can name every species of tree in Southern Africa. Owen has neatly typed card index records of hundreds of trees on this side of the Masongola plateau. He plots their exact position using a grid reference and a compass and measures their heights with a small brass clinometer which he keeps in a buffalo-skin pouch. He assesses the state of the bark and the leaves and is especially interested in any signs of branch poaching. If he notices any particularly impressive butterflies, he makes a note of that too. If he can, he catches them in a net and kills them by piercing them with a dressmaker's pin through their abdomen. He is particularly fond of the large swallowtails for which the plateau is so famous, and has rows of them in deep glass frames: all pierced through the heart and neatly labelled in Latin.

The women's wards are a row of rooms opening onto a covered verandah and Tilda Mason steps out from the large cool room they have given Florrie – there are two beds in it but there are few patients admitted today and the sick child has it to herself. Away from the fans and the old thick walls, the air outside is hot: infused with the smoky heaviness of the bluegums. People are already saying it is hot enough to rain: but that is not serious talk, only a first step in the ritual of waiting – everyone knows there are weeks to go. Tilda wants to speak to her little boy, Jack, sitting cross-legged in the shade of a big tree. He is drawing the Jacaranda flowers scattered around him on the thin dry grass and hard earth. He likes it that his mother calls them 'Jack's trees' and he is absorbed in making a picture for her: carefully tracing the outline of the small trumpets.

– Which is nearer: purple or blue, Mummy? Chimwemwe doesn't know and neither does Tilda.

– He must ask Daddy. Daddy knows about trees. Perhaps, for now, he can get a good colour by mixing the blue and the purple.

They try this: smudging the colours together with a finger but the effect is disappointing. It is turning to brown.

– It is still a lovely picture, but he has been here long enough now: the whole afternoon, says his mother. Chimwemwe should take him home and see to his homework, bath and bed. Jack can come with her now into Florrie's room and say 'sleep well' to his sister. Mummy will come into his room, even if he is sleeping, and kiss him goodnight when she gets home. But for now, Doctor Philip wants her here, just a bit longer, to look after Florrie.

Jack starts to protest but the girl nods and is already picking up the coloured pencils, placing them correctly – points all facing one way – in the moulded plastic grooves of the tin. Chimwemwe is always very careful about such things.

Jack clings to his mother – he wants to stay – but the nurse is at Florrie's door calling for Tilda with fast urgent syllables.

– Take him home now, Chimwemwe; tomorrow; he can see Florrie tomorrow. And the nurse's words are now close to a scream. Tilda yells to Chimwemwe to get the child out of here and the pencils are scattered again amongst the blue flowers as the girl scoops away the long-legged boy onto her hip and runs with him down towards the main road.

Florrie lies on a grass mat on the red polished concrete floor. They put her there when they tried to restart her heart. She does not look dead at all. Tilda reaches out and touches the small tuft of frizzed hair in the centre of her daughter's forehead. It feels exactly as it always does: springy; wiry; Florrie. She likes to touch it as part of the good-night ritual. The child's pale blonde hair lies in damp half curls around her face and neck as it always does after a hot day – this is normal. Her little hands are curled beside her head, that is how she sleeps: hands up, don't shoot, I surrender – how she always sleeps. Tilda lifts the child's right hand: the back is bruised purple, where they could not find the vein to put the drip in.

Just before Jack was born Owen had said – Remember Tilda, my children will be Africans not expatriates. Not temporary residents. No one can take chloroquine all their life? You're different Tilda; you're not an African: but your children will be. This is their country.

This afternoon they had stood back as the young Scottish doctor pumped and pumped at the tiny chest. She wanted to tell him to stop: he was hurting her child. When he had raised his head – his hands still crossed over Florrie's heart – and looked up at Tilda: everything became still and quiet. It was then that Owen roared – that awful primeval cry of pain, and the African nurses moved quickly away out the room, And Owen went too.

And now she is left alone with her daughter. Philip, the doctor has gone down to finish his shift at the General Hospital – there his patients are three to a bed – he has been up and down the potholed road between the hospitals all day because of Florrie. She can see he is exhausted but he will come back. There is a lot of paperwork involved in the death of a white child.

Tilda kneels beside Florrie who is still and pale and beautiful. Afterwards, this is what they will all say to her and to each other: the doctor; the nurses; her own friends. They will say how beautiful she looks – as if this is something not be expected; as if death should make her ugly or frightening; as if it makes a difference what she looks like. But she is beautiful.

She doesn't know what to do. That terrible howl of Owen's – she has never heard any human cry like that – has drained her of all her will: silenced grief. There is no answer to it. Tilda feels something like anger: it is as if Owen has claimed all the pain for himself and has taken it with him – wherever he has gone to. And she knows with horror that she has no part in that cry: it was for more than Florrie. Her husband is a white bushman: everything he has ever believed in is up for losing. But this grief should be theirs: it is not his birthright – today there can be nothing more than Florrie – and he has no right to take it away.

She is numb – she knows this happens – she does not know how to feel. But this time will not come again and she needs to find grief in it while it lasts: the doctor will come back soon and they will make arrangements. She wants to bury Florrie tomorrow – she cannot leave her in the hospital mortuary: a frightening place for a little girl. But she knows there will be other children there. A month ago her cook came to tell her that his first-born son had died. And that too was malaria. She was saddened when she heard that of course but – This is Malawi, said Owen. Children die. Less often at this time of year though: everyone knows there is more malaria in the rainy season when the mosquitoes breed easily. But they say too that dry season mosquitoes are the worst: they have to be strong – they have to survive; have to preserve and carry the poison from one season to the next – it stands to reason. It is all, says Owen, about survival. – You have to beat the little bastards at their own game, he says.

It is so hot, so hot. The only thing that must happen quickly in this tired season is the burying of the dead. But Tilda wants to look at her daughter; it is too soon to let her go. What kind of mother leaves her child without some tears? She thinks of praying and she does. But she has been praying all day.

The Toyota is still parked on the driveway: Owen has taken the pickup. She takes out her camera and tripod and sets it up next to Florrie. She is a photographer. This she can do well. She selects her portrait lens and focuses. She wants a shallow depth of field: it needs to blur out the stained cellular blanket. Florrie's head is turned so that the left cheek resting lightly on the pillow is thrown into shadow. She will accentuate this with more light on the upper cheek. Tilda moves to the window and adjusts the blinds. Always focus on the eyes – that is where the life is – the key to the character. But the drawn down eyelids are the deadest feature of the child's face. She squeezes the lens until the curve of an eyelid is perfectly aligned in the split field. Through the lens something about the child's mouth draws her attention for the next shot. The lower lip is thrust slightly, imperceptibly forward – she sees things through a lens she does not see with just her eyes – and the mouth is drawn to the left. It is this asymmetry which gives life to the face. It is the expression of a determined and confident child about to tease; about to smile. What is Florrie dreaming about? Whatever it is – it is the opposite of fear.

She stops the lens right down: she needs a shallow depth of field but a long exposure. She is glad she has brought the tripod. She wants to get every strand of hair just right. She shoots and shoots. A roll of Fuji colour then one of black and white. She is utterly absorbed in the task. She is doing what she knows. She is taking pictures. In Africa you take likenesses with care; you ask – *ndikujambuleni?* – even then some people will not let you; they believe you are taking away their soul.

The lights have come on in the town below. The doctor has come back: he offers to drive her home – no, she will be fine. As she is getting in the car, Tilda makes out Jack's drawing pad and his coloured pencils scattered on the grass. She picks them up and finds the tin too. One pencil is missing from its place. She sees it half buried in the soft blue skin of petals covering the parched and dusty soil. The colour is lost in this half-light. Some flowers stick to her fingers and the pencil and she shakes these off and snaps the tin shut. She will be back before bedtime. She will tell Jack about his sister. And then she will develop the film. She will not show Owen these beautiful photographs. One day she might show Jack. Perhaps when she herself dies, someone will find them then.

In the days following the funeral Owen takes to driving the pickup long miles into the bush – sometimes for days on end – though it is too hot to drive. He brings back cuttings and saplings and quantities of seeds. He plants out the specimens in pots and in the flowerbeds around the garden: it is the wrong time of year for this but nothing can quench his zeal. Water is rationed but he has the gardener hosing morning and night. Someone at the university can freeze dry seeds and he spends days labelling these and putting them away. The collection of swallowtails grows: a man at the market is kept busy making the deep box frames. Owen tries to interest Jack in butterflies but gets angry when the child cries and won't put the pin in. Jack cannot know that his father is saving Africa.

When he wakes up from another nightmare on another hot night, Tilda soothes the child – cradling his head in her breast. She needs him to know how precious he is.

– She will look after him, she says. She will keep him safe. But she knows – and why should this not be his nightmare too – that she did not keep his sister safe. Her head aches all over but she understands that this – even this – is not yet what loss feels like.

Afterwards, she steps out onto the *khonde* and listens. The silence is filled with the ringing night – cicadas and frogs. The ringing never stops. Here, the ringing is what silence is. It is too hot for the dogs to bark. Something moves in the dry yellow grass. Somewhere miles and miles away there is the merest slice of light in the sky and a faint rumble of thunder. The clouds have been gathering and passing over the plateau for days in a final taunt. Soon things will change and the air will fill with the smell of the hot steaming earth.

Tilda watches and waits for the rains.

Part III

Silences of Home

Envisioning the Silences of Home:
Four Poems

Jack Mapanje

When You've Never Lived Under a Despot

When you've never lived under
a despot admit it, his minions never
made you dance in the flaming heat nor
forced you to offer your last cow, goat,
sheep, chicken, egg or the coin hidden
in the loin-cloth purse around your

waist. When you've never lived under
a despot concede, you've never known
the deadly concertos of his dancing witches –
Women's League, Youth League, Young
Pioneers and their 'spearhead' this and
'spearhead' that, which whipped up

his support. When you've never lived
under the despot's minions confess, you
will never feel the hit squads that bumped
off the political rebels they fashioned for
their president for life, forever corrupting
the nation. When you've never been the despot's

self-appointed heir, henchman, hanger-on,
accept, you'll never hear the silences that
slit the throats of Life President's suspected
traitors as ruthlessly as they slashed their
prolific 'rebel' maize gardens, burning down
their 'disloyal' grain-bursting granaries

assassinating and bombing his 'rebel'
exiled families for exposing his official
corrupting silences. When you've never
truly lived under a despot or his vicious
dogsbodies acknowledge, otherwise you
will tend to fail to spot the larger plot.

Henry Masauko Chipembere's Mango Tree at Mtundu, cheChiwaya's

This fig tree at Mtundu, cheChiwaya's was
robust, dynamic once – political arena, court,
market; chiefs and their elders chewed our
cases in subtle riddles, proverbs, narratives
there, fishmongers milling about bamboo
and reed stalls, trading sun-dried utaka, usipa,
zisawasawa, nchila, mcheni for salt, sugar, beads;
women in cheerful calico offered spirited prices
for their sweet brew, babies on backs munching
banana bread baked in banana leaves. And
this mango tree, this arch rebel standing tall
beside the fig tree at Mtundu, cheChiwaya's
hasn't it weathered agonising Young Pioneer
butts over the years? But when figs, mangoes,
like their rebel hero, finally fall to earth, will
clouds gather and swallows swoop and turn –
presaging another bitter-sweet fruitfulness?

The Grain that Keeps Leaving its Silos

If you've been watching stories of bags
upon bags of maize disappearing from
people's silos without trace into diverse

bureaucratic bellies only to be sold back
at pitiless profits to the dying folk or across
the borders to neighbouring countries; if

you care to remember the history of these
silos – how those American drones spying
from above almost blew them up once,

'thinking' they were another Cold War
nuclear plant from the other side; if images
of emaciated men, women and children

dying have moved you and, perhaps for
once, you thought these were just another
batch of our African jokes gone sour – I

suggest you watch the state president's
governors, who, though democratically
elected to supplant the last of our despots,

continue to build despotic structures to
safeguard their authority from the truth,
drenching the fig trees all over the land

in fierce storms about the people's universal
fertilisers, starter packs, 'aged' treadle-pumps
and maize from silos sold across the borders.

And should your conscience fray, impotent,
as skeletal hands cook the last green elephant
grass to fight the famines politicians deny,

do not despair, rather, craft on the riddles,
proverbs, narratives our ancestors in their
numerous voices showed us how years ago;

sing, even cry yourselves sore, until maybe
your tales stop the pledges crossing borders
or block the grain disappearing from silos!

Prayer for Paramount Sages

Dear spirits of our fathers and
mothers, these spirals of denial, world
without end, what paramount sages will
you send now to repair the invisibility of our
rural and urban folk, forever suffering, forever
dying, whatever brand of political
regime takes the arena?

And my dear, dear youths who must know
our time in these never-ending liberation
struggles is done, why do you still clutch at
the tail-end of the western gimmicks going:
big brother this, celebrity that, idol this,
reality that, hand-driven radios, hand-
wound computers – all purporting

to heal the pain we event for the ordinary folk?

And these red, black and white ribbons,
these bands, these 'make poverty history'
doggerels, when will human life without
a God, without a plot, translate? The reality
is the West never fulfils whatever it pledges;
their global village was never meant for you;
the West wants you wherever you are forever!

Why, therefore, oh Christ, why
do you gaze elsewhere for answers
here? Why don't you see there will be no
better time for you to enter the arena
with finer voices and perhaps give
the ordinary folk the dignity
they've always deserved?

Fred D'Aguiar

Calypso
(After D.W.)

Calypso king bounce back after an absent spell,
I know you miss his wisdom and his sexy smell.
He got an aroma that lingers like an empire.
You crave his bohemian lyrics, their rapid fire.
I only come in answer to your desperate call
For a man with cahones to address this squall
Between a global monster and a flea outpost
Resisting the overtures of empire brute force.
For that gripe I got rhymes coming out my pores,
More than Microsoft Windows have doors,
Or the government's corporate tax breaks
Lining rich pockets while the breadless eat cake.
Politicians decide in the people's domain,
God and big business to kick some foreign
Backside, but what they trust and worship
More than any just cause or shiny battleship,
Happens to be paper and green, with the onus
Less on The Almighty than on a hefty bonus.

Their forced aid amounts to a flimsy plaster
Slapped on our deep cut that's bleeding faster
Everyday; we being Third World people, so-
-Called, transported west to reap and sow
As slaves. What history left us there's no cure
For or if there is – as Diana's song implores,
We don't want it, index it with plunder.
Western leaders keep our beelike cause under
Your queen beds until we ripe to come
Out and sting every company scheme some
Board reckoned on as profitable gain;
Democracy dishing out poison, not Paine.
Don't fill us your sugarcoated pills anymore,
It killing us with interest and we still poor.

I break up long time yet I breaking it down,
Exposing all them politicians acting the clown,
But behind we back they brandishing knife
Swearing they love us as they take our life,
Or should that be wife, husband, son or daughter;
Politics and religion equal poor folk slaughter.
The spirituality every poor person needs
Got sweet FA to do with a make money creed.
The poor extract the spiritual from simple acts
Such as helping a neighbor in a scratch-my-back
And-I'll-scratch-yours gesture; a little thing that deep
Shows the poor own power. Why should they be meek?
Many ants make an army, one weak, many strong.
The day ants grasp their strength that day anteaters gone.
Pardon my doomsday-calypso-singer persona,
I sold platinum when the message was the medium, Sony.
I try to keep my role as sage, light, and I try to laugh;
Like Mr Average, I lime, labrish, hang and gaff.
But there comes a time when a man must speak
Headlines, when he should not turn the other cheek:

This Prolonged War For Oil And Revenge For Nine-Eleven
Founded On Too Many Lies And Cost Too Many Living.
Empire building for profit should be exposed –
Paine gone bad when used for company expos.
Corporate types with mansions and stretched limos,
Stretch Paine's logic on the rack; these doyens
Of global trade convert Paine to dollars and yen.
A rubber necklace is too colloquial an end for
Buzzards that feed on honest, local vendors.

2

The Caribbean scattered like pearls off a broken necklace
One of the sea goddesses broke when she tossed her face
Towards the sun to clear salt-wet hair that strayed
Over her eyes, she cursed and the curse stayed
Since it was a goddess who said it, and Europeans
Found the beads and cleared them of all the Indians
And then because theirs was a different kind of curse
The Europeans put back the blight of centuries
Of African slaves then indentured Hindus and Muslims.
When I stare into the Caribbean Sea I glimpse
That same goddess working up a storm of grief
For her curse that lasted so long from an act so brief
As an off-the-cuff utterance. Now there's a god
For the bad weather that rips trees off the tripods
Of picture perfect postcards still worked by slaves
From civilisation's cradle to civilisation's grave.

You hear the news about the government? A man ask
Me the other day. I take my time to address the ass.
How can you mix government and new in one breath?
Who died and made you chief left you smelling of death.
Sometimes the spirit catch me so, though I crumble
Something in me always fit and ready to rumble.

When I hear people talk about politics like it new,
I come to the boil and start to fret and stew
About how politics with its polymorphous tricks
Pretend to walk soft but mostly wield a cocomacca stick.
Ain't change since Rome when Caesar fall to Brutus
And Nero fiddled at home; all that trickle down to us
Like it happen yesterday. How can new share space
With government and not make me shout disgrace?
Like Marley with three teapot hats on his dreadlocks,
His reggae reasoning traps power in a headlock.
He gelled epistle and liturgy as a Rasta prophet,
When he Chant Down Babylon, power lines atrophy.
His lyrics defend the poor; he's their champion.
History fed his brain; poverty was his champagne.

3

On the Peter's Projection America's a smear
On the blue ocean planet's steamy underwear.
American power and American might in a century
Of nuclear fright, amounts to a skid mark on greenery
Left out of the fridge to wilt. I mean to say as plain
As my tongue can spell it that America dish out pain
While the rest of the world must swallow for the sake
Of world peace, as parents, trying to accommodate
A spoiled brat having a gigantic, red-faced tantrum,
Throw up hands and watch since what's to be done?
Parental hands wringing on the sidelines did not settle
Well with students whose Internet savvy upset Seattle.
They threw projectiles at the G8 summit accord,
Made the evening news and got a police record.
It takes the youth to remind us of basic decency.
They crossed the bigwigs who showed no leniency
When it came to stamping out democratic protest,
Quick to deploy Marcuse's state repressive apparatus.

What's gross about America remains its excesses:
What bulge, super-size egos and thirst for gasses.
They should bottle the stuff their leader spouts nightly
On HD TV since hybrids can run on tripe sprightly.
The rest of us mortals can't take anymore, please,
We've caught stuff from American's emission and sneeze.

This in no way exonerates the smaller nation
Like the over-governmental Caribbean basin,
They walk wide-eyed into the trap of consumption
With shopping sprees to New York, Miami and Boston,
While their country's majority don't have two red cents
To rub together, they mortgage the future of innocents
With high interest loans from the IMF and World Bank
In whose back pocket they shall remain for life, which, thank
Goodness, is not forever. So pour the rum and let
The music play, we got life now, forgive and forget.

Don't think about continental Africa's plight
Aids, war, post-colonial rule, and no daylight
Between western elites and their home grown progeny,
Both jet to Harrods and breakfast at Tiffany's.
Africa pulls on my heartstrings more than I can name,
More than any place, Africa's the disapora's shame,
Our hurt when we got nothing to complain about
But can't fathom why sleep won't start after lights out.
Children beckon with limbs lopped off by freedom fighters,
Blood sparkles in the conscience of diamond gatherers,
Tribes war over borders drawn up in 1885 in a European plot
That slashed the face of Africa like history's Harry Potter.
Like history's fool bloody Africa gets played
Again and again like an ugly virgin that can't get laid.
Africa, cradle of Mankind. Africa, the skull in profile
Mercator mapped. Africa, the child, Europe the paedophile.

4

Don't make me rant, stop me before the calypso spoil,
Don't stand there pop-eyed, while I scream Cod Liver Oil.
Lend a hand; join the band; beat some pan; show me hope,
Show you understand. I'm a man. Let me bubble like soap.
I going come back stronger like curry that goes in hot
But comes out hotter. Don't rush me. This is my slot.
Rush me if you're a Russian. Hurry, hurry, make bad curry.
As a watched pot never boils so a calypsonian won't flurry
If he or she's worth his or her salt or gestalt as the case may be;
Keep up if you can, I switch from politics to psychology.
Ear to the ground, tongue in my cheek, glint in my eye;
Sway in my hips, my fingers click; you laugh till you cry.
I'm in the driving seat so my eyes need to be clear,
Otherwise trouble, nobody going anywhere
Fast, we one plait on one head of a scalp of thick hair
See that and avoid ideological catacombs of living dead,
Learn from Afros, locks and canerows of political heads
Even bald heads in top hats dream hair long as twine.
Lyrics keep flowing with the beer, spirits and wine.

I take the back route since I done dead already,
I pick up roots and shake my head like Solomon Grundy.
I play the part Sir John Harrington played for hygiene,
Except mine would be on the moral and ethical scene.
He invented the toilet, I invoke satire; both have the effect
Of raising our hind quarters higher, ask Pope, Swift or Beck.
I coming to face the moral Lilliputians like a Gulliver,
Like the ads say about the rock 'n roll pizza, I deliver.
I lift people's collective spirit and cleanse their soul,
But ears and eyes must open, hearts prepare to get scold,
A scalding of the character, a whipping back into shape,
A butt-kick of the highest order that nobody can escape.

Daylight on the city, after my visit, looks spic and span,
The national grid polished by ethics arranged for steel pan.
I empty churches, confessionals with nothing doing
Whisper to themselves, I provide people moral gluing.
Nuff said about me but one more thing about the climate,
My mission to lift our times above our cousins the primates,
Won't end with my song, not for long if we're to win
Against corporate malfeasance and out and out sin
Committed by governments who dispose of our young
In armies of conquest for greased palms and oil towns.
By the time I stop this, how many babies will die
From diseases we can cure? So many children lie
On dirt floors and give up brushing gangs of flies
From the corners of cracked mouths and empty eyes.
Too many for my liking, too many to count or excuse,
Each of us makes a choice to ignore, each must choose
To do some small thing over and above helpless despair,
We can vote, write, place calls, march and cheer.
If the revolution must be televised by CNN and NBC
Let it be on time, on our terms and commercial free.
Let the red wounds of roses sit in ready gun barrels
And look like a real possibility that could end quarrels
Rather than optioned for a film, T-shirt and chain
Store like Che, the holocaust, Palestinians and rain
forest. I could go on, I will go on for a little longer:
Rhetoric is an infusion that ruins or makes reason stronger.
But only because the times make me turn in my grave;
Just because the children, the innocents, need to be saved
From the beast of consumption, the monster of capitalism,
The consumer of the planet till the planet capitulates.
Join hands and sing with me, we shall overcome,
The will of the people adds up to a powerful sum.
Draw a line in the sand; let's make that last stand,
For the benefit of all species here to share one land.

5

I know when I strike this note I sound like John Lennon.
I realise many poets consider this tone a bit of a lemon.
But I past caring about what poets think, poets who try
To write but don't read, poets who plant their poetry
In commerce, who lack hearts and who don't give a fart
About anyone or anything; who vacate morality from art,
For some privileged notion of self exploration and some
Heady hunch that their art is private: it's only (as one
Private said to another about army life) as private as our
Privates; poets navel-gazing abdication of the Muse, her
Tried and tested and true calling to bear witness to what
We sense and must say, no matter how little lands in our hats.
Poetry requires us to cuddle wasps, speak in tongues
On behalf of the downtrodden, to the hard ears of big guns.
I say this with a crystal memory of falling in love
With a woman who I could not get enough of
Nor she of me; our world revolved around the bedroom,
We filled each other's head, swept cobwebs with a broom
Of desire that lit our bodies with a perpetual fire and thirst
For each other so much so I felt I was going to burst
With happiness, I felt blessed and worried the flame
Would die and I would never find this kind of love again.
And it did run out but not because anything died inside
It was just that the everyday has a way you can't hide
From for long, of encroaching, as the mundane
Keeps knocking with a reminder of the, well, yes, mundane.
Love isn't all you need but love gives courage its fuel.
Love quickens the heart and lightens the belly.
At any point during that affair I felt I could face an army
For a cause or for nothing, I felt so contented, so dreamy.
Love is a drug that feeds flesh, mind and spirit;
Desire soothes the brain and wrecks the body's habits.

Once you've loved that deep it's hard to settle for less;
You keep looking for the holy grail of earthly happiness.
Then you start to see the world falling short on every count
And bam! Before you know where you are you've mounted
Some public statue in a square and it's about to fall
To herald in some new day in some free for all.
Call it politics or opportunism, call it what you must,
But it's built on love and love is all I can trust
In this life to bring about what I can't see for all the wealth
In this world, but what I feel has to happen for the health
Of the planet: the prudent use of nature's finite resource,
And the countless poor – help them till they become scarce.

6

I must confess love kept me from politics with its drug,
I went mushy in the head and lifeless as a rug.
It wasn't until I had my fill of the woman and her island
Ways that I began to notice headlines from other lands.
One picture of a naked Iraqi on the end of a girl-soldier's
Leash and one word, Guantanamo, started solder
From my eyes from that moment my lover's cunt
Bored me stiff and I began to view my erection as a runt
Who never felt quenched, a pig who would eat until sick
And eat that up only to vomit and eat again in cyclic
Gourmandising Babylonian decadence – yet I nosed
There for truffles and lapped up what I found close
By until I could map her sex with my eyes closed
And the thought of her made my tongue hunger most
Of all hungers and that's when I felt I could die right
Then and not bother about dying, die without fright.
Soon after that more news trickled into my porous head
And like a sponge I began to soak it up and feel bad
For the woman-soldier, for Abu Graib's void space.
I wanted the soldiers to answer but most of all I placed

Blame on the government that called them up and could
Find no better use for them than as fodder and firewood.
She begged me to stay and held my thighs as I walked off
Shaking my legs free. I ignored tingles, stirs the warmth of
My loaded groin, watering tongue and giddy head.
She stopped calling my name and cursed me instead
'May you never find pussy as sweet again but sour
Every taste and every time you try, may you cry for
My pussy but all you got is a second rate squeeze
And nothing but missionary for your sins and disease;
May your seed always fall fallow and arms ache
For child but all you get is doubt and another's mistake
To care for and nothing of your own but a stake
In your heart for me and what I offered and what you threw.'
That was the last I saw her and every word came true.
I think of her when I hold another and I come up sour
Mouthed and impatient to finish and grab a few hours.
I tried for children for years until I fooled my mind
That the years were just days and I had bags of time
When the clock was about to run out with my options
And my draw-string seed sack dry up its populations.
I dived into party politics and bore all the cost
As compensation for love found and love lost
Through my fault and no one to blame not even
The government who had nothing to do with me leaving
Her when I did in answer to a call without origination
Or end, the call of my conscience whose tintinnabulation
Won't be ignored without a knot forming in the stomach,
One you can't untie or fool or decorate or flummox.

7

The light on the Atlantic scatters silver coins,
Under the sea light bends its back in benediction
To an element as pliable as it, deeper still white bones

Of dead slaves form a road back to African homes.
It's a road I walk in my sleep and the bones don't mind
My feet on them, in fact, they hold still for my kind
Who come in search of peace and find we can hold
Our breaths underwater and make our way to pots of gold
At the end of certain rainbows with politics and love,
Birth of the Cool rather than any nation or a God above
As guides, and the moral of the story is the story
Itself and there's no story without this morality.
Calypso king have his say and he thank you for the loan
Of your eye and ear and now let him go back alone
To his resting place free of bureaucracy and bad omens
Where he can reunite with his love and the only woman
Who played *Astral Weeks* and made months pass in a day
Just when he had settled for Exodus and L.K.J.
She took him back and said nothing except to undo
Her curse and then his buttons and zip and you
Can imagine the rest, and if you can't, think of wreaths,
A reef knot of lips and limbs, a Bombay mix of breaths.

Beverley Naidoo

In Our Time
For Salgado's Children, All Our Children

Assault assail annihilate assassinate
Destroy despoil devastate desecrate
Deface defile decimate detonate
Explode execute eliminate eradicate
Murder massacre maim mutilate
Wound waste vandalise violate
Ravage wreck ransack raid
Pillage plunder rout raze

Syllables spurt, bright with rage;
The charge of hate ignites the page.

Revive refresh restore repair
Nurse nurture cherish care

Our words are few and too genteel,
Unequal match for striking steel.

Sing a song of innocence
Three babes lie open-eyed;
Thirty thousand men with knives
Shall soon come marching by.

When the babes are hungry
And they begin to sing,
Who will stay the butchering hands,
Restrain the hatchets' ring?

Is it very different
When death screams from the sky?
When those in suits press buttons,
Plot charts as victims die?

Sing a song of innocence lost
Of hate unleashing lust;
What kind of species pulps its own
Grinds life and love to dust?

(Commissioned by Barbican Education in response to
Sebastião Salgado's exhibition of photographs *Exodus*, during
the invasion of Iraq in 2003. The photograph referred to in
the poem is of three Rwandan orphans at Kibumba Number
One Camp, Zaire, 1994.)

Two Poems

Phillippa Yaa de Villiers

Cold Fire

Television: you have stolen the fire
of our dreams. Your flickering face captures
imagination, you've eaten entire
generations, and spat out their raptures
like bones. And now our souls are hostages,
bound by pain that's forgotten how to weep,
and automatic laughter, foraging
for comfort in the white noise we call sleep.
Like feral beasts, we fear when darkness falls,
we seek the certainty of the herd, hide
to warm hide, horn to horn, the tribal call
as feet beat the myth of life into rite:

now passive spectators watch silently
this cold fire, uniting humanity.

New Skin

Beware the bright snake slow on a branch,
its old skin, transparent and thin, behind it.

The forest holds its breath: the snake looks painted,
still life, still, alive and dangerous.

The new skin is a scar. A scar is the emblem of healing,
unbearable the air's weight on a new skin.

Its fangs are primed to poison curious fingers:
beware the fearsome sensitivity of a new skin.

Beware the bright snake of a new dispensation,
remember the sting of skinned knees: you also know

the pain of change. Lost equilibrium. The strike,
fangs bared, blood forced to the surface.

There are no accidents. Calamity, evolution all produce
the same results. The air on new scales weighs the same

as a landslide in Chile. Change is not a personal attack.
If you turn nature into the enemy, you will lose.

Beware the bright snake slow on a branch,
its old skin, transparent and thin, behind it.

Three Poems

Dorian Haarhoff

Magnified Moment

one morning I saw it,
watching my father shave
in his swivel mirror.

one circle showed his human face,
aged, grey, wrinkled, nicked skin.
then he swung it on its axis.

in the reverse moon
his face magnified,
bristles thrice their size,

pores a diamond design.
a blood river cut
through a wild sea.

over his shoulder
in a ring of silver,
I saw a thousand fathers rise,
large as gods.

The Red Earth Jar

in the sweat of December '45,
when I was one,
a peasant led his camel
to the mountains of Jabal.
he dug up sabakha, top soil,
at Hammadi Caves,
for his garden.
his steps echoed
in the chambers
of buried Egypt.

his blade intoned a strike.
he scraped the contours
till an urn emerged,
half the measure of a man.
he traced its neck and buttocks,
wondering. his blood-beat up,
he raised his mattock
and smashed it to starry shards.
he resurrected no gold, no silver,
but papyrus, Coptic script,
caught in loose leaf and leather,
one embossed with an ankh.

his camel carried his find,
dumping it at his mother's oven.
she fed straw and shredded leaves
to the fire. the rest she gave
to the village priest
who passed it to a reading one.

so, word by word,
the news spread throughout the land.
Ali al Samman's mattock
unstopped the Gnostic gospels.
from a 2,000-year sleep,
the jinn leapt from the red earth jar.

Bird Hide – Langebaan

this hide, with its bench
and window ledge
where you kneel,
to rest your elbows
and cup your hands
to the twilight,
serves as communion rail
in this cathedral of lagoon and sea.
the setting sun is choir master
to the fluttering of a thousand wings.
a flamingo in priest's robes
blesses the wine-water
and the bread mulch in the reeds.
I ingest in silence
the bird's cry and the sea roar
and taste the salt marsh on my tongue.

Three Poems

Graham Mort

Eucalyptus

The night-light shivers, sweats
vapour, flickers to our
childhood fevers.

Its flame rides liquid wax the way
a mariner's compass needle
floats on mercury.

We lie still, breathe incense, feel
the room's mural of shadows
soft as ibis feathers.

I love the smell of Eucalyptus
you say, your parched palm
almost burning mine.

We go like dead pharaohs in our
barque of a bed, sails full of a
desert's funerary breath.

Camels gaze calmly, the Nile's
waters rise and whisper near
enough to trail a hand.

That's an owl calling from the elm
that lightning broke; unlucky
in all this African dark.

The night's a jackal lapping stars
from our window; its studded
tongue curls around us.

I stare out, think of continental drift,
the Earth's plates sailing apart,
the way we've circled each

other all our lives like a planet
and its moon, and not known
which was which, even

before we met, fell sick together
or lit this flame in our temple
of unknowing

how we became or why
or where we'll navigate
tonight.

Indigo

Today we woke in the ether of indigo: the
    scent of my first jeans near black and
stiff as sails and cool for once in '68 – this
    cotton throw bought late one day in Kano
where slaves were sold a lifetime ago. Trade
    winds and cowries and the sword unfurled its
quintessense of oldest-glowing darkest blue.

Nigerian sun liquifies that memory to a
    blinding yard where children gathered
barefoot and curious to see the white man
    watch their fathers work the dye pits
sucking their teeth to draw each steeping
    piece from sunken lungs for air to stain
its elemental earth-breath blue.

The men watched for what I might do
    or buy or say; a woman laughed in Hausa
covered her face from this rich stranger
    so quiet inside his pale of Englishness;
the Emir's cavalry rode past on Arab mares
    their sinew knotted taut as ropes where
benzene vendors haggled in the road.

How could I say I wanted only to watch
    them lift each dusky sky-patch purpling
their red gloves to the wrist? Not to buy or
    be troubled by wealth – except the riches of
light sinking on the city's ochre walls – but to sit
    in shadow as cloth rose and fell in their fists;
all held in the scorched palm of the sun.

What was I thinking? I should have remembered
    the chill here, how the stove is raked and lit
how we're undone each day by seeping cold
    waking to north country rain rinsing green hills
beyond this attic room where breath casts mist
    into early day the way I've seen the
sun burn off fogs of equatorial night.

Now I'm drowsing in this old scent of Africa:
    new Levis and unexpected youth, vestigial
warmth, those memories soaked in past days.
    Or maybe I'm still asleep, not yet changed by
Africa or chemistry of indigo, the cloth I brought
    thrown back from body-heat where you were
sleeping a second or a century ago.

Labourer at Kololo

He is cutting stones, the red soil of Kololo;
his blood a heated blade, his palms pale
with sweat in the Kampala sun.

He slices weeds, a crust of earth, the old
hide of empires, the panga's blurred steel
flensing steam-heated air.

He counts hours, then years: rainy seasons
on an iron roof, cassava crops, the sun's
stare through slashed matoke leaves.

Black kites float in the depth of his eye, scavenging
a white-scorched sky; a marabou stork flaps
the drumskin of its hunger.

After noon's vertical sun, thunder clouds will plume
those seven knolls, boiling from afternoon heat
into crazed night-time rain.

He stares to the lake's mist, to hills where Kabakas
pitched their courts until death wrapped another
jawbone in barkcloth and silence.

A beetle pincers a grub, its buffed armour scurries
over the man's bare feet, earth's rusted promise,
the broken stones of his labour.

Meg Peacocke

Jato

Jato is dead, so he won't be scrambling
to an internet café to tell me
for himself. When I try the frequencies,
what comes through is just the Guernica scream
you can't switch off; but I think he's laughing
about the mosquitoes of Maroua
still trying to suck out his shadow blood
till he's slapped himself rigid. Since the world's
turveyed to a negative, it's child's play
to handle a Kalashnikov; and when
the midday sun comes hammering at doors,
who can you trust to say what's light, what's dark?

Jato Nyanganji, journalist and poet.

Three Poems

John Lindley

Nervous in Nairobi

There is no known translatable expression
for the answer I give
to the dazed and dangerous gaze
of the kids in this part of town –
not in Swahili, Urdu
or even post-colonial English.

It is a wordless reply,
a series of brisk and businesslike strides,
a fast scanning eye,
a hand in a jeans' pocket
that denies the notes within.

I have never before chewed gum
quite this confidently
with quite this nonchalance.

Crossing Borders

Top-cornered in my bedroom window,
the bleached shadow of a man splitting wood
in a bone-coloured moon.

With no message tonight undeliverable,
with a dry wind from Malawi
coughing through cables and moving in my room,

I marvel at everything; understand all:
how the number seven translates into Chichewa
and back again and is pronounced 'magic',

how my screen is the skin of a tribal drum,
how legends resonate in the bowl behind it,
how the stories quietly chant in Microsoft,

Top-cornered in my bedroom window,
the bleached shadow of a man splitting wood
in a bone-coloured moon.

With no message tonight undeliverable,
with a dry wind from Malawi
coughing through cables and moving in my room,

I marvel at everything; understand all:
how the number seven translates into Chichewa
and back again and is pronounced 'magic',

how my screen is the skin of a tribal drum,
how legends resonate in the bowl behind it,
how the stories quietly chant in Microsoft,

how my modem hums with folklore,
my mouse skitters across borders
and is still at the moment it lures from speakers

the sound of blessings for the sake of the living,
the splash of palm wine and chicken blood
for the sake of the dead.

'Problem'

It's not those without legs that are,
but those with.
It is, anyway, a too small word
for those on stumps,
cupped hands extended;
a shamefully inadequate word
for their plight
but a word just big enough
for tourists like me,
accompanied by uninvited guests
who promise me cut price anything
and, let's face it, are merely the small bites
of non-toxic bugs
that possess neither the threat of malaria
or of prostitutes with bodies to die for.

Three Poems

Beth Webb

Eating Mama's Roses

'They bring water here
to wash your hands.'
Our dipping fingers meet
in quick-silver,
then shaking drips
we are ready to eat.

My students discuss Eliot
Over cushions of tasteless foo-foo
And oily-fried sweet potatoes.

'He is obscure
and simple at the same time,'
one says.
'Give me one towel, hey?'
his friend replies.

I chew caty-caty
which I cannot swallow
and brush aside
dancing,
fornicating flies.

The barred window is open to the street.
I smell sweet smoke
from rubbish heaps
and ignore the lad
who's selling trainers
between tables,
his wares neatly balanced on his head.

Noise,
smells,
intellect,
and accents too rich for me to unpick.
My focus drifts
'lah-da, lah-da,
blah wa her? Her too dah.
How? Da lah-ha!'

Absently I chew bitter leaf and agree.
It is too hot to think.

Red Balloon

Red balloon,
tied with cotton
around the dusty brown wrist of
a tiny child
dressed in a fatigued
bridesmaid's dress.

Her father laughed.
She just looked at me
bemused
with huge eyes.
I walked away
encumbered by my white-lady
largesse.

Woman in Red

Woman in red
watches herself in mirrors
as she rolls proudly by,
ham on ham.

Before her,
she carries a majestic belly
and behind, an arse to match.

She knows she is admired,
and smiles.

Two Poems

Graham Fulton

Owl Interrupted
Kwazulu, South Africa

Pitch-dark safari. Moonscape road. Icicled bones.
A smirr of rain
is trying to make us feel at home.
Trembling impalas. Peepers reflecting
light from a hand-held battery lamp.
Frightened scurriers fixed in the beam.
Ostriches mincing about on a hill,
sulking zebras behind a bush.
Snuffling warthogs. That's about it.

Seems I'm growing weary of Africa;
something to do with a state of mind.
Bored with beautiful, sick of exotic,
pining for chewing gummed-pavements of Scotland.

Life-drained drones with Buckfast and drugs.
Methadone babies, tanning booths.

Then unexpectedly, almost missed –
a plate-faced hitman, binocular-eyed,
still on a stump – staring at us.
Deathmachine-calmness, gallus assassin.
Some type of owl; I'm not sure which.
A thump of deep, ferocious wings.
Spotlight following, finally, gone.

The only one I'd seen in the past
was propped on a pole in Paisley zoo.

Out of place in a place like this.
Monkeys drumming across the lodgeroof,
monkeys trying to raid my suitcase.
Stilt-legged giraffes. Yeah, whatever.
Too much air. Too much big.

Seems I'm growing narrow for Scotland –
praying for hood-ruled-precincts and ranks,
cokehead hyenas caught in the beams.
Chinese special noodle boak-pools.
Natural habitat, cave wall art.
Trolleys thrown in the River Cart.

Distribution

Kwazulu, South Africa

A junction of nowhere that's not on the map.
XY co-ordinates, clearly unmarked.

A railroad track ploughs through this village;
narrows, with purpose, to far directions,
satisfied hubs, wealth of nations,
restless East, FTSE West.

Women with baskets balanced on heads,
patiently, wait to ford the sleepers.
Hands on hips, practised poise –
the females here do all of the work.
Market tables, figs or maize;
distribution of food and weight.

A long untouchable shuddering freight train takes forever to pass.

We spy from the first world side of the glass.
Hunting-pack toddlers raise their knees,
mime an attack, jab at our faces,
stamp as they grin against our bus.

Syncronised thrusts, born for war.
They know these tourists aren't worth a damn,
cannot provide clean water, a plan
to dodge extinction from this day to that.
Last-born daughters hold out their hands.
Money, sweets, mouths to feed.

Cattle burrow their senses in bins.
Thin men gossip in small dark shade.

Henning Pieterse

Mapungubwe*

I

The throne on which the still king sits,
polished stone, looks south.
A warm wind remembers voices
of bodies swarming in the valley.
He sees me, mining within walls,
finding artefacts for my poem,
blue glass beads, a pot shard,
remnants of a golden sceptre.
I slowly raise his huts from the soil,
scaffolding for my verse,
rooms filled with ivory and coloured glass
adorning his dancing warriors.
As high as their rusting spears
his warriors crouch in their grave.
(Slowly, dust seeps in
through the frames of my poem.)
A gilded rhinoceros horn grows blunt.
(Lock the doors and seal the windows.)
The soil becomes embalmed
with his warriors' fragrant bodies.

II

From his hill the king could rise
to embrace the wide horizon
of trees, animals, people
held in the kraal of his folded arms.
He could dream of the north, like me,
where out of the blue a stone kingdom rose,
time's smooth column of silence
growing between circular walls.
Within the grooves of ancient ditches
I find copper, beads, an eyelid porcelain,
a shell that came from a longboat
drifting on the river from the east.
Warriors, yellow with autumn,
dance across my poem to the north.
Few were to return, the only remains
sunk into stone-quarries of memory.
The king would stare at a baobab
in flames on the plains;
at a boat engraved near the river,
anchored in a rock.

III

Once awake, I will turn to the west,
my verse against the flow of water,
I'll see the wind caressing river's muscles,
copper-smooth, smooth.
Past rocks like elephant graves
will I walk; thinking of a rhinoceros
which rises slowly and stands a while longer
to sniff the wind from the south.

Voices will sing within clay walls
and huts, black against the fire,
will watch the king who listens
to the fading rumbling of feet.
He would see a bird that climbs the water portal,
a bird that settles itself in stone,
steadily staring at me from dust,
from conches, coins and porcelain.
One day, in the dream-time,
a longboat will reach my shores.
And the rowers will lower their oars
into the glass-blue water.

*Mapungubwe: archaeological site on the Limpopo river,
northeastern South Africa. This civilisation reached its peak in
the thirteenth century AD and was involved in trade with China
and Arabia. It is widely regarded as the precursor of the Great
Zimbabwe Civilisation.

Reviews

The Testament of Gideon Mack
James Robertson. Hamish Hamilton. HB. ISBN 024114325X. £17.99.

No Fireworks
Rodge Glass. Faber. PB. ISBN 0571226272. £10.99.

I Have Heard You Calling in the Night
Thomas Healy. Granta Books. HB. ISBN 1862078130. £12.99.

Since the cultural commentator Tom Nairn first made his small but passionate *cri de cœur* that he would not rest until he had seen in Scotland the last kirk minister strangled with the last copy of the *Sunday Post*, many, many things in this country have changed in ways that even Nairn might not have anticipated. One huge change is the massive loss of influence of religion, *qua* the Church of Scotland, on national life. In our new Scotland, the official religion no longer occupies the place it once did. It barely manages to raise its voice in public discussions, and in this multi-cultural and multi-faith society, it should not feel too hard-done-by having to compete alongside other faiths and religions. The time when the Church of Scotland had any influence – perceived or real – has practically gone. And this makes the appearance of James Robertson's *The Testament of Gideon Mack* all the more remarkable. Perhaps London publishers imagine that in Scotland the indigenous population still defines itself tribally, along pre- and post- secessionist lines, and that these same Scots continue to warstle daily with the question of 'hou mony session-clerks can be sat on the point of a needle?' It is again a long time since the Kirk of Scotland reigned supreme, and an even longer time since Scotland could be called a theocracy, which happened for a very short period during the seventeenth century.

I do not mean to offend Mr Robertson, nor would I wish to be unappreciative of the time and effort he has expended on creating this novel. But I think that *The Testament* comes not only as a huge disappointment, after his two earlier successful works, but also largely as an irrelevance. A monumental irrelevance. However, it is possible that *The Testament* is very subtly ironic, and that in his examination of the emptiness of religion, Mr Robertson writes too subtly for me.

That *The Testament* is indebted in many ways to Hogg and also to Stevenson is obvious, but unlike Hogg's *Private Memoirs and Confessions of a Justified Sinner* or Stevenson's *Weir of Hermiston*, it does not strike me as an account of any struggle between good and evil, whether along traditional religious or post-religious lines. This is because there is no struggle in the narrative. (Except that for me it was a struggle to read.) Within the Judeo-Christian codes, notwithstanding his morally uncomplicated, adulterous liaison with his best friend's wife, Mack's graver sin appears to be that of sloth, which is perhaps more theologically interesting in all its ramifications: Mack is presented as being just too lazy to believe, and his journey – if that is what it is – into unbelief, seems remarkably effortless and unfashed. His passage into unbelief – or his developing awareness, or admission that he no longer believes, or has ever believed – just happens. It involves no inner struggle and no spiritual battle. No angst here, no existential crisis, no feeling that he is, in the words of the Old Testament prophet, '*minus quam nihilum*' – less than nothing.

And it is not for any theological or metaphysical reason that Mack propels himself into his supernatural experience; rather it is his stupidity that takes him towards freedom and annihilation, when he launches himself off a mountainside to rescue a dog, so taking himself for three days down into a dark place, where he sups with the devil. Nor can his ordeal there be described as his dark night of the soul.

Although *The Testament* is peppered – and annoyingly so – with references to contemporary news events, giving it the verisimilitude of the up-to-date and the impression of a narrative unfolding in or close to the present, neither this, nor the Reverend's symbolic corrie-fistedness, nor the appearance of his own Stone of Destiny, seem to be effective. These are clumsy devices, heavy and intrusive.

There is one compelling section in the book, however, the funeral of Catherine Craigie. The description of this exuberant and trangressive event is equal to some of the best writing produced by South American exponents of magic realism, and in itself would make a brilliant short story or perhaps an aurally rich radio play.

Writing on a less grand scale, though, I think, more effectively, Rodge Glass, in his debut novel *No Fireworks*, describes with great pathos and humour one week in the life of a Manchester Jewish family. Seven days after her death and burial, Evelyn Stone, mother, grandmother and great-grandmother, a nominally unbelieving woman and a veritable matriarch, is still full of surprises. The person at the receiving end of most of these surprises is her son, Abe. A thrice-married, 61-year-old history teacher, on long-term sick leave with a hopeless drink problem, he is looking for salvation – other than in the shape of a whisky bottle. Besides, the fireworks the whisky used to create, stopped happening long ago.

The surprises he is receiving take the form of post-mortem missives from his mother. 'So here we are – and maybe you'll pay a little more attention to me now I'm dead', begins the first, which is headed 'Know Thyself'. In the second, his mother abuses him a little more, and reminds him that 'you may have escaped the cold hand of God so far, but every day He picks more victims, and one of these days He's going to pick you…' In her third letter, Evelyn uses more reverse psychology to goad Abe into some kind of belief: 'Dear Avraham – (and there was my first mistake. Father of a multitude, indeed. Leader of the tribe. You can hardly lead yourself to the bar and back!)'

These letters, coupled with his increasing doubts about his sanity, lead Abe to embark on a spiritual journey, first into the arms (and between the thighs) of a new barmaid at his local pub, then to conversations with the Rabbi, then into training as a volunteer in a Church of England charity shop, where, perhaps not unsurprisingly, he has a massive heart-attack.

While recovering, he comes to the realisation that his spiritual journey must take him to Jerusalem to make *aliyah*. He escapes from his hospital room with his 14-year-old granddaughter and non-verbalising boyfriend in tow, getting as far as the airport. Except, a different kind of 'spiritual ascent' has been reserved for Abe. He 'goes out of existence, and out into the great sprawling warmness on the other side', where there are no fireworks.

I Have Heard You Calling in the Night is altogether a different kind of writing. It is a memoir that charts Thomas Healy's harrowing journey from his days of fighting and drinking to his growing understanding of the possibilities of redemptive grace. It is also a powerful piece of story-telling, because it does tell a story, about one man and his dog. Confessional in tone, it sounds like the examination one makes of one's conscience. And stylistically, this work is like plainsong; it is simple and unadorned. Its power comes from its simplicity and it qualifies as a piece of devotional writing within the long tradition of contemplative literature.

Michael Lister

My Life as a Man
Frederic Lindsay. Polygon. PB. ISBN 1904598722. £8.99.

Shadow of the Serpent
David Ashton. Polygon. PB. ISBN 1904598706. £8.99.

Stories told and stories untold are central to Frederic Lindsay's *My Life as a Man*. For Lindsay, best known in recent years for his Edinburgh-based DI Meldrum series, this is a fictional return to his native Glasgow. The story begins with the anti-war rally of February 2003, but most of the narrative centres around a much earlier experience in the life of the protagonist, Harry Glass; one that defined the person he has become. It is Glasgow in the aftermath of the Second World War. Homeless and penniless, newly-employed Harry asks his boss, Bernard Morton, for his week's lying time. On receiving the money, Harry realises that he has also been sacked. He retaliates by driving off in Morton's car, thereby appropriating both Morton's wife, and a briefcase belonging to his brother Norman. Determined to recover their property, the Morton brothers – and other interested parties – pursue Harry and his passenger across Scotland. Finally the fugitives find shelter in the remote farmhouse of a reclusive couple, August and Beate, but this is not the haven it appears.

Thematically too, Lindsay is covering old ground. There are echoes here of his first novel, *Brond*, which also concerns a naïve protagonist embroiled in a situation beyond his control. The older Harry who narrates the story, realises that he is 'a creature of chance and time'. For his younger self, the journey was a rite of passage from which he emerged a lover and a man. In truth he was an unlikely knight-errant, who has little knowledge of Mrs Morton's world: 'I don't even know which bloody spoon to eat soup with.' With 'no future and no home' he had little to lose, a 'nobody'. But, although untutored, he is not the nameless dupe of Lindsay's earlier work. Mrs Morton too shakes off her passivity and regains the self-respect she had lost in her marriage to the brutish Bernard. But although Harry may have proved himself in a Darwinian world governed by 'the law of the jungle', personal survival dictates that he and his wife become 'a nation of two'. There is a different kind of loss involved in this, as the older Harry is quite aware.

Like his sinister creation, Beate, Lindsay 'tells a good story', but this is much more than a thriller. His understated prose belies the power of the ideas he is scrutinising. Set both at the time of Britain's war with Iraq and in the years after the Second World War, this is a contemplation on the nature of evil and how far humans are prepared to go to achieve their ends. For Harry the real revelation of World War II was that what 'united men' was 'their need to hurt one another'. 'After the Nazi death camps,' he observes, 'all of us knew that Europe of the high culture was a continent of torturers.' The story examines why people kill and at what point this becomes a viable option for those who consider themselves civilised. It exposes the masks which are part of our civilised persona and what happens when these are stripped away.

Aficionados of Scottish crime writing will already be acquainted with the narrow wynds and cobbled streets of Edinburgh's Old Town and the contrasts between rich and poor portrayed by David Ashton in *Shadow of the Serpent*. Familiar too are the dark rages and relentless quest for justice of its fictional detectives. The latest of these, Ashton's Inspector James McLevy, is already known to listeners of BBC Radio 4. He is not, in fact, a fictional character; the real McLevy's police career commenced in the 1830s. His reminiscences, *Curiosities of Crime in Edinburgh* and *The Sliding Scale of Life* were widely read, influencing Conan Doyle in his invention of Sherlock Holmes. Now, Ashton, an actor and dramatist, has produced a novel incorporating the same characters as his radio series.

Ashton's McLevy is a much bleaker creation altogether than his rather bombastic real-life prototype. The fictional version is a flawed character, his existence, 'a struggle between personal human frailty and a desire to serve justice'. His story begins in 1880 with the brutal slaying of a prostitute. The murder has links to a case thirty years in the past, when McLevy was a young and inexperienced constable. His failure to solve the earlier crime makes him all the more determined to succeed now, but 'The Serpent' is a shadowy and elusive creature from the upper echelons of society – possibly even one of the most powerful men in the land. This too is a feral world – the lines between predator and victim deliberately blurred. Wolf-like, McLevy stalks his kingdom of Leith. The son of 'a mad woman and an angel', he lives in constant dread of inheriting his mother's insanity. He is both blessed and cursed with 'an ability to empathise with the criminal mind' which might one day lead to 'demonic possession'.

This is a darkly Gothic novel and Ashton has worked hard to create a sense of period. We find here the stock fare of much Victorian sensational fiction with lunatics, opium addicts, bawdy houses and mysterious women. The real villains of the piece however are those with power – the politicians. Politics is 'the dunghill upon which many a cock has crowed'. The setting of the action at the time of the 1880 election, with Gladstone and Disraeli leading opposing parties, allows plenty of scope for ironic observation, and this background is meticulously researched. Nineteenth century 'scientific' advances, we are reminded, included barbed wire and dynamite. There is a wry humour too in the inevitable comparisons with contemporary experience. The novel is intended to be the first of a series, and with a pilot script commissioned for Scottish Television, this could prove lucrative. There are times though, when the narrative almost buckles under the weight of period detail and the cumbersome prose Ashton seems compelled to employ. Such excesses of Victorian style might be best left to rest in peace.

Margaret Beveridge

Tsotsi
Athol Fugard. Canongate. PB. ISBN 1841955663. £6.99.

'Tsotsi' is a South African slang word for a thug modeled after the ruthless American gangsters of 1940s cinema. Athol Fugard's title character is as ruthless and unsympathetic as any of the villains he may have aspired to be. Through his seamless interweaving of extreme violence and moral bankruptcy with moments of compassion, redemption and outright bewilderment, Fugard creates a challenging story that gives no easy answers.

Certainly, the power of Fugard's novel rests in its protagonist. A man-without-a-past, Tsotsi lives day-to-day, killing and victimising whomever he must in order to keep himself alive. The archetype perhaps is nothing new, but it is Fugard's way of rendering his anti-hero that is remarkable. To say 'his name was the name, in a way, of all men' brings us to the uncomfortable realisation that Tsotsi is a sort of survivalist Everyman. Fugard does not apologise for his character's abhorrent tendencies (as he stalks a cripple through the streets, say), but in dramatising the backstory of White expansion into (and the subsequent destruction of) Black townships throughout South Africa he garners an almost unwitting sympathy towards his otherwise deplorable protagonist. Fugard complicates his story by introducing a vehicle for change when Tsotsi, while attempting to rape a woman, has a baby thrust into his hands. Still, the author does not sink to simple plot devices. Tsotsi keeps the child in a shoebox, then leaves it in a ruined building. Ultimately, the child facilitates the return of Tsotsi's childhood memories, though, and he finds his conscience can no longer be utterly ignored.

While it sounds a traditional tale of redemption, this novel is anything but. Anecdotal histories engender care for even minor characters, only to have them tormented and killed by Tsotsi and his gang. Even after the protagonist begins to consider right and wrong in their own terms, he still chooses to steal and coerce. Situational dialogue on matters of decency or the measure of humanity is deftly undermined by the introduction of some new, daily horror. Through it all, Fugard's prose draws colour and life from the most pallid details and unsentimental visions. The result is a complex landscape of birth and death, damnation and redemption. What places this novel far above others of its kind is that Fugard never reduces his message to the idea that comfort may rise from desolation; instead he remains committed to the harsh reality that answers do not come easily, if they ever come at all.

Stephen Lackaye

Escalator
Michael Gardiner. Polygon. PB. ISBN 1904598625. £8.99.

Michael Gardiner's *Escalator* is written as if an insider could view his life as an outsider. His characters are a lively cross-section of Tokyo life: foreigners, students, homeless, salarymen, office ladies, high school girls, housewives, punk rockers – and each is treated as insular and special. Many of the story's characters are filled with despair. It is as though Gardiner has reached his hand into the crowded streets of Tokyo and abstracted its innermost thoughts – and yet one wonders if the Japanese think of themselves as Gardiner does, or if they did whether or not they would admit it.

Gardiner's stories explore the myriad of lives possible in Tokyo, always with compassion and careful detail. Often these stories, like 'Out', 'Fast Track', and 'Living' are about escape. Soto, the main character of 'Out', is a middle-aged 'talent scout' looking for women to work his Hostess Bar. As he stands on the corner – grading women as A, B, C or unacceptable – he fingers his back pocket which holds his secret bankbook: an account with enough money to move abroad and start a new life. In 'Living', a teenager decides that, due to his lack of Highers to enter university, his best bet is to work his way through Asia. But without a degree he cannot obtain the proper visa status and ends up hauling freight boxes off ships. It is there – within the forbidden contents of the boxes – that he finds escape. In 'Fast Track' a female office worker on an aeroplane examines her situation and finds herself in the toilet, her hand 'clutched at a square of toilet paper: the paper was trembling slightly, and for a second she wondered why toilet paper would shake.' She takes a pill to relieve her anxiety but finds herself, 'feeling, suddenly, numb. She was still willing the plane onwards, onwards, back to the place she'd started from… wondering whether her contract would last the length of her journey.'

And often the stories that deal with escape and uncertainty have characters that wonder how they arrived at their position in life, because they'd followed all the rules and done as they were told. They had attended 'prestigious universities', had good jobs and are on the 'fast track' to success, but somehow it isn't enough for them: these characters are still in despair. It is in stories like 'Fast Track', 'Escalator,' and 'Debut', that Gardiner imbues these characters with his own speculation of their fears and doubts, more so than in his stories about redemption and love which seem to flow more naturally.

For example, in 'Deai' a law student finds a dating site on his mobile phone, meets a girl and after forty minutes the couple has agreed to have a relationship. While strange, 'Deai' was much more believable than the stories which feature a character's remorse over their chosen life path because of the innocence and ease in which 'Deai' is told. Similarly, 'Kodoma' offers a unique opportunity of insight. Two people sit across from each other and engage in speculation – each longing for, and making incorrect assumptions about, the other.

Gardiner's stories are told in such a way that, although the reader is learning about the setting of modern Japan, the information doesn't detract from the pathos of the characters. Overall I was highly entertained by these stories but wouldn't recommend them to anyone who was so in love with Japan that they were blind to her faults. 'Escalator' does not attempt to make excuses.

Amanda Moody

Matters of Life and Death
Bernard MacLaverty. Jonathan Cape. HB. ISBN 0 224 07785 6. £14.99.

Matters of Life and Death is the latest volume of short stories from the Belfast born author. This is MacLaverty's fifth collection of stories which, along with four novels, comprises a body of work that dates back to 1977. *Matters of Life and Death* contains eleven stories in total; seven are set in Belfast, with other locations including the west coast of Scotland, a Dublin nursing home and a university campus in the American mid-west. The fact that only three stories address the Northern Irish situation is testament to MacLaverty's enduring significance, and his relevance beyond any narrow identification as a Troubles writer. The title, *Matters of Life and Death*, provides the collection with a sense of thematic coherency which, as was the case with Yeats, suggests that questions of mortality and decay are becoming increasingly important to the more mature MacLaverty. 'The Assessment' details an elderly woman's Sisyphean task as, through a cleverly fractured narrative, we witness her attempts to deny the early signs of Alzheimer's disease. 'The Clinic' functions as a memento mori, a study of fear and stoicism, when an older man is forced to visit hospital for that most ominous of events, the routine test. The title of the collection is indicative of the deep poetic resonance that has become the hallmark of MacLaverty's style. With precision and stunning economy, it connects between the deeply serious with that which is most trivial. It points toward the volume's underlying preoccupation with the everyday and the ordinary, and their profound, harrowing and often compassionate revelations that exist just beneath the surface of our experience.

In terms of the Troubles, 'The Trojan Sofa' and 'A Trusted Neighbour' (reminiscent of earlier stories like 'Walking the Dog') evince an identity politics that is irrevocably intertwined within the daily fabric of Northern Irish life. MacLaverty's literary apprenticeship in the company of the much famed 'Belfast Group' of the 1960s (Heaney, Longley, Ormsby et al) suggests a useful context for considering his artistic engagement with the post '69 conflict. Like the best Northern Irish poetry, MacLaverty's stories are disarmingly perspicacious. They often turn on a single image, arresting the gaze, and compelling us to reconsider what is exorbitantly horrific at first glance. 'On the Roundabout', a story about a brutal and misdirected sectarian attack, meditates on the repetitive, futile and ultimately meaningless nature of the North's sectarian pathology. This darkness however is offset by MacLaverty's interest in the untold, the unremembered and the unfamiliar, and his continual attempts to map a Northern Irish landscape that has been systematically ignored by mainstream representations. 'Belfast Memory' is just that, a poignant remembrance that is no less effective for its lack of obvious narrative teleology. Three decades of living away from Northern Ireland (in Edinburgh, Islay and now in Glasgow), and perhaps under the influence of Scottish Literature's own highly attuned ear, MacLaverty is masterful in rendering both the nuances and artistic possibilities of Northern Irish speech. The funniest moments in the volume provides a cunning indictment against certain global versions of Irish kitsch. Installed in a Dublin nursing home, the sharp Northerner, Mrs Quinn, remarks about the Southern accent: 'I hate the way they talk. Like honey dripping. Smarm and wheedle – like they can't do enough for you, like you're the Queen of May... I never could stand that Terry Wogan.'

MacLaverty is equally confident beyond his regular canvas of Northern Ireland. Often it is the outsider that knows us best, and in terms of Scotland and MacLaverty, there is both an intimate knowledge and a welcome degree of critical distance. 'Up the Coast' sees him revisit the familiar territory of his Booker short-listed novel *Grace Notes* (1997). It is a violent story set against the rugged landscape along the west coast of Scotland. Like Warner and Banks, MacLaverty is alert to the ambiguity of the scenic Scottish tourist trail: it is a source of rich artistic inspiration as well as a breeding ground for isolation, despair and atavism.

The contemporary literary climate, increasingly affected by literary prizes, book groups and best seller lists, is one which would inevitably marginalise the short story. *Matters of Life and Death* is a potent reminder of the arresting potential and fundamental importance of this unique literary form. In this artistic space, where poetry and prose reach out toward one another, MacLaverty is one of the finest practitioners writing today.

Matthew McGuire

Bad Shaman Blues
W.N. Herbert. Bloodaxe. ISBN 1 85224 728 2. £8.95.

It seems ever more apparent that we are in the midst of a marvellously rich period in Scottish poetry. We may have lost a number of the great figures of the past in the last two decades, but the new poets who have emerged during that time are now maturing into writers of genuine importance. Among those, perhaps the most naturally gifted and prolific is the Dundonian, W.N. Herbert, now living in Northumbria.

No longer a young pretender, Herbert is now a poet in his forties with a sizeable body of work behind him. His fifth substantial collection from Bloodaxe in the last twelve years, *Bad Shaman Blues* again demonstrates such mastery of form and invention, of language in all its registers from the self-consciously 'difficult' poetic style fashionable in certain English language circles today to the bawdy Scots street song, that the reader turning from poem to poem is beguiled and bemused by the sheer unpredictability of the diet – as if the chef presented beluga caviar and pie'n'chips side by side on the same menu, without explanation or apology. The shifts of mood and subject can be abrupt and frankly disconcerting, almost as if there were a number of different poets, or at least a number of Pessoan-like alter egos, at work here.

So at first sight *Bad Shaman Blues* as a whole appears far from the thematically-linked and stylistically-coherent volume, and is possibly overly dependent for its identity on the thread of experience of the poet – but on closer reading, recurrent images and themes emerge, such as that of the divide between the barbaric and the civilised, with parallels drawn between Herbert's life in the proximity of Hadrian's Wall and his visit to the Great Wall of the East. These are issues that have occupied the poet for as long as he has been publishing. Here the wall itself acts as symbol for the ultimate impossibility of translation, even easy transition, between different states – and by inference, the sister tongues of Scots and English:

> The difficult words can't make it through,
> their letters swoop and clatter in the grass like armour;
> their questions fall on the other side
> of the unguarded Wall, their great marks sprawl
> untranslated in the barbaric grass…   ('Over the Wall')

The reader senses that these difficulties of understanding are of deep personal concern to the poet, as if he is never truly at home in either leid, or on either side of the divide. In a poem ostensibly about Kurt Schwitters' sojourn in Cumbria, he writes:

> To settle where they couldn't gauge his worth,
> to build the wall that sealed him off from fame,
> to tear himself off and stick his self down...   ('Schwitters in Ambleside')

Is Herbert here speaking also of his own situation, a Scots language writer of supreme gifts exiled among English poetry, where readers are ill-equipped to grasp the full glorious depth of his invention? Identifying with the German and equating the building of his 'Merz' works as an artistic act comparable with those great walls of political boundary-drawing – as if the making of art itself is the creation of a barrier to shield artistic intelligence and sensitivity from surrounding barbarism? It is at least interesting, if not significant, that one wall of the last of Schwitters' Merz works, which he called the *Merzbarn*, is now in the Hatton Gallery in Newcastle.

The idea of the barbaric, uncivilised world surrounding the embattled artist is taken up in other poems, notably the superb long Scots sequence entitled 'Rabotnik Fergusson' which has echoes of the Divine Comedy, with Robert Fergusson exploring Hell and Heaven, as well as outer space. He finds a dystopia in which the great Scots poets of past ages are fallen craiturs, ignored by the universe, their words stuffed up their arses in an act of mockery, while in Heaven the throne is filled by none other than his fellow Dundonian poet:

> This Grecht McGonagall, ye'll learn
> huz neither knack nor need fur feet:
> this universe adores his lets,
> and him alane frae here they read ...   ('A Lullaby while Resetting')

It is as if this is to be understood as the ultimate insult to the true spirit of poetry and Herbert's employment of a broad range of traditional verse-forms in this sequence displays his virtuosity, demonstrating the very skills that McGonagall so lacked. Elsewhere, he turns again to the Tayside tragedian, but this time places him not as the king of 'upstairs' but of down:

> McGonagall... wiz no a woeful poet bit a thingummy far worse
> a juggernaut of doggerel, the laureate of hell...
>
> ('Ode to the "New" Tay Bridge')

And so the title of the collection and the overarching concept comes ever more into focus – we are told on the rear cover that this collection laments 'the role of contemporary poetry: reached for in trauma, otherwise ignored. The poet as shaman cuts a reduced and comic figure'. That it most certainly does, in a wonderfully shambolic chaotic manner. Though it occasionally addresses tabloid concerns and utilises the language of the fowk, *Bad Shaman Blues* is in essence another appeal for an intelligent readership on the part of 'high art', shot through with a sense of inevitable defeat for all its glorious achievement. This last mood is made explicit in a few brief confessional moments scattered through the collection:

> ...the way I travel
> is equal to the way I live:
> inept, withdrawn, and half-unravelled,
> too full of neediness to give;
> barely witnessed seeing fiercely
> never heard or very nearly.　　　('Air Sibir as Shamanic Flight')

And being W.N. Herbert, the writer offers the same sad sentiment in Scots as well as English:

> Eh'm thi less travelled, unravelled man
> jist a-waitin fur a slogan in thi new Bedlam
> Eh'm thi man ootwith thi language, wi the slanguage fuhl o baggage
> and Eh carry meh sowel in these three bags...
> 　　　　　('Sofia City Blues')

Herbert's work continues to be among the very finest in contemporary Scotish poetry. While he may not as yet have attained the broad fame of some peers, such as Jamie or Paterson, his potential is at least as great. While others have integrated their Scottishness by means of a few choice words or expressions embedded in an otherwise English voice, the work of W.N. Herbert bristles with difference, dilemma and paradox, with doubleness and alterity. In this alone, his work is perhaps a truer reflection of the current state of this United Kingdom than that of those more celebrated. He stands astride the wall.

Robert Alan Jamieson

Scots in the USA
Jenni Calder. PB. Luath Press. ISBN 1905222068. £8.99.

The English incomer to Scotland who prepares for, as it were, citizenship, or rather acceptance as being on-side, should prepare, as I did, by reading histories, good and bad. The bad, more than the good, often carry the myths that shape policy and behaviour. One finds a lot about 'the auld alliance', or rather the invocation of the phrase, and 'being closer to Europe'. But Jenni Calder's fine book amply demonstrates that the main alternative connection to the English has, from the mid-eighteenth century onwards, been the United States.

Calder has been quietly at the very heart of Scottish cultural life for many years. She has written or edited over twenty books, including poetry, mainly on Scottish matters, most notably biographies of Robert Louis Stevenson and of Naomi Mitchison. And last year saw a semi-autobiography, *Not Nebuchadnezzar: In Search of Identities*. For she was born in Chicago and her early school education was in the USA, and then England; and in her early career she spent three years in Kenya. But there was never any real doubt about her identity, only that she always had an interest in and feeling for the Scottish diaspora – as did her father, David Daiches, for the Jewish diaspora. So she put her last years before (active) retirement to good use, when Head of Museum of Scotland International, to read and travel for this book.

She begins by invoking the obvious, but the obvious is often forgotten or taken for granted: that the seaways from Glasgow point westward and Glasgow grew on the American trade. Yes, she does not forget the triangular trade, as economic historians contextualise the slave trade; nor the role of Scots in the anti-slavery movement and then, almost as if in penance, the missionaries to Africa to this day, not just David Livingstone. She shows both how the political principles of early republican America appealed strongly to many Scots, in the days when the United States was a beacon of liberty to the discontented and disenfranchised all over Europe; and she shows the social appeal of American society to those who would 'better themselves'. That phrase, 'better oneself', is found in many letters home from migrants to North America, and it had both a social and an economic context. She quotes Daniel Defoe as saying: 'the Union open'd the door to the Scots in our American colonies, and the Glasgow merchants presently [i.e. quickly] fell in with the opportunity... I am assured that they send near fifty sail of ships every year to Virginia, New England and other English colonies in America.' And Walter Scott in *Rob Roy* has Bailie Nichol Jarvie extol the

Union as 'the treaty that opened us a road west-awa yonder'.

She tells the tale of ordinary immigrants of whom some records survive, if dug for with imagination and diligence; and also of those of fame like Andrew Carnegie, who was so proud of his native land and gave back so much to it. He deserves to be remembered for more than his treatment of his workers, when he connived at the Pinkerton men gunning down his armed strikers (Alan Pinkerton himself a Scottish immigrant). His success and philanthropy showed how close the Scottish belief in the poor 'lad o'parts', who could rise high by honest hard work and education, was to 'the American dream' – that any honest man can make it to the top. But I have always liked the joke of 'Mr Dooley' (John Finlay Dunne, the Aristotle of the Chicago Irish): the pan-handler knocks on Carnegie's door asking for a glass of milk and a bread roll; Carnegie tells his butler that they must not disadvantage the man in the competitive struggle of nature, so no handout, but 'Give that man a library'. Self-help was a common American and Scottish mythic ideal.

Robert Owen did emigrate but Congress invited him to address them on the New Lanark model of enlightened capitalism, and he saw the USA as the proving ground for 'New Harmony' – which failed for mundane reasons, as did the settlement in Tennessee attempted by Camilla and Frances Wright – largely forgotten early Scottish feminists. Long before that, many from the Highlands left for the Piedmont of Virginia and the Carolinas, and many moved on into the mountains, particularly favoured by (or the last refuge of) Ulster Scots. Here Calder could have noted how many of the feuding mountain boys kept out of the War of Independence and resisted attempts by both sides to conscript them; and how in the 1920s they defied 'the great experiment', prohibition, to the extent of armed battles with revenue officers.

Also I think she misses the degree to which the recent revival and new founding of Scots-American societies and festivals has been a reaction to the American-Irish celebrating so loudly their sense of dual identity. Some have played a dangerous political game – NORAID versus the Ireland Fund. But Scots-Americans have to struggle against, not indulge, the romanticised tartan Kailyard image. Calder shows that the great Smithsonian Institute was not only founded by a Scot but embodied Scottish ideas of popular education. But she cannot have seen their doleful 'Scots in America' exhibition of two years ago, which seemed as if VisitScotland had curated it – would that Jenni had. This is a well-researched and serious book – well-written, albeit simply – not a sentimental journey.

Bernard Crick

The Invention of Poetry: Selected Poems.
Adam Czerniawski. Salt Publishing. PB. ISBN 1844710912. £9.99.

Adam Czerniawski lives in Wales; he writes in Polish and in English. Wales is not Czerniawski's simple domicile, I suspect, but a place of vantage; on the antipodes of the so-called great events, and histories, he lives his quiet poetic moments; he's got the time, and the view, for reflection. Wales, with her oneiric landscapes and her enigmatic language, is best suited to that. His thoughts and his themes are universal; he is a detached poet (*in exile in English*); he needs and he capitalises on this out-of-placeness and this distance.

He draws on various traditions: classical, religious (Christian lore as well as others) and all rather gnostic. He relentlessly looks back on the past – his childhood in Poland, adolescence in Lebanon and Palestine, his arrival in England are his constant, inexhaustible source of inspiration.

His poetry can be subtle, unassuming, but it can also be poignant, sharp. His poems are direct and down-to-earth, yet strangely exalted; he uses simple words in complex and sophisticated ways. His imagery is evocative, suggesting a different depth, 'illegible like [scribbles on] a worn stone', and mystical, like undecipherable signs on a wayside cairn – a relict of unredeemable past.

When you read his 'Ode to Youth', written sometime in the 1970s, you trace his words with your fingers as you follow them with your eyes; they are almost palpable, and you want to take that one peek 'over your shoulder' and 'return to the toys lost in the sand.' That, and more, is Czerniawski's irresistible allure; his charm.

In his poems at times he alludes, rather than explains, as in 'Love' composed in 1996 where he speaks, in beautifully structured verse, of the myth of Orpheus and Eurydice – his lover, but he mentions no names. He can also be lyrical, as in his 'Oxford', another 1970s poem, where he states in the end that: 'sometimes' as if silence were music 'one has simply to say nothing.'

I cannot overlook one other important factor, namely, the poems' translator, Ian Higgins.

Higgins, a poet himself, has been translating Czerniawski for years; he captures the true sound of the poet's language. And the task, to be sure, isn't easy. Czerniawski's is poetry based upon melodic structures, *jazzy* to be precise. It is, as argued by Bogdan Czaykowski, another Polish poet, 'characterised by a deliberate polyphonic dissonance' thus quintessentially, it is unmelodic. Higgins not only sees this, he grasps it and converts it into English.

There is a note of sadness to Czerniawski; his tone is at times nostalgic, even, funereal of, for instance, 'annihilated childhood' – a childhood buried in a diasporic past. There is, in his later works, an untitled poem, almost an epigram: 'He arranged his life, but not his death', reminiscent of *fraszka*, a form preferred by Kochanowski, another Polish poet, a seventeenth century master. 'Fraszka' (from Italian *frasca*: a joke, an anecdote) is a humorous form, composed, speaking melodically, in key-major. I detect in Czerniawski's piece that sense: a wry humour over a life lived well and an unavoidable passing. But 'not everything ends', the poet says in the book's epigraph: poetry withstands time, it is eternal, and thus is the poet. This book spans the poet's entire life – the formative and the most recent years, and it celebrates just that.

Piotr Wesolowski

Life Mask
Jackie Kay. Bloodaxe. PB. ISBN 185224691X. £7.95.

The obsession with mask-wearing lies in its anonymity. Identity concealing is mischievous, playful, and sexy, allowing people the opportunity to act out of character without the fear or pressure of judgment. Shakespeare employed the use of masks to represent lust, hypocrisy, and stealthy desire in his plays. In pagan fertility festivals masks were worn to hide a potential lover's appearance, so that the sexual attraction was about the immediacy of sensory perception. Criminals wear masks to disguise themselves from the law and doctors wear them for protection from infectious disease, and in both cases masks have become synonymous with their occupations. As much as masks are about camouflage and containment, they are also about role playing – establishing a new identity through character acting, growth, and metamorphosis.

Jackie Kay's 'Life Mask' is a healing process that deals with the loss of love and a reunion with her father. Kay's mask is an emblem of shelter, nurture, and transformation. It is a place she withdraws to, looks within, where she hides herself, and becomes the transformative cocoon that she emerges from. 'Life Mask' explores the narrator's ability to adapt to the betrayal of her lover and redefine her own image by renewing familial ties. The poems that are most successful allow the narrator distance from the personal nature of the subject matter. For instance, 'There's Trouble for Maw Broon', is derived from the

Sunday Post comic strip about a family of nine living in tenements, stretching the money as far as it will go, and finding humour in the generation gap. In this poem, written in dialect, Maw Broon becomes suspicious of infidelity after Paw Broon begins to sharpen his appearance, 'It crept up on me bit by bit, / till wan sudden day I saw Paw wis fit.' Paw Broon's traits that originally annoyed her became the traits that she began to miss, 'he didnae belch and say/ *Guid fir me*! He didnae tut at the TV/…He lost interest in fitba/ He started eating his veggies raw/ It was mair than I coud staund.'

This poem enables the narrator to identify her own experience with adultery without getting lost in specifics, by placing it onto well-known fictional characters, so that the reader can immediately sympathise with the situation. The poem is ultimately about the narrator's fear of change and Maw Broon is a mask that allows these feelings to surface.

Midway through the collection, in the poem 'Two, Medicine Man,' the narrator looks to her father for healing, comfort, and advice. In this poem, that is more like a shamanistic vision quest than a dinner outing, her father appears to her disguised behind a healing mask, 'I can see his eyes through the mask/ he cooks words in a clay pot, /rubs them rough into my forehead / he shakes my head back and forth. / "You can walk through fire, you won't be burnt."' After the healing ceremony, the father begins to explain why he has been absent from the narrator's life, 'He takes off the healing mask and replaces / the father mask. 'Those were the beer- / drinking days. All the women loved me.' Then he transforms into a bird saying, 'You are evidence of my past sin. / You have my genes,' and flies away. Instead of faulting him, the narrator admires this freedom because she has inherited it.

'You have left this big hole like a manhole / in a dark childhood street, the stank pulled up; / strange things crawling down underneath. / I am afraid of chucking new people down the hole.' These are however small mis-steps in what is an otherwise wonderful collection of her work.

Life Mask is a collection that should be read slowly and compassionately. It is an intimate portrayal of abandonment, and at times, hope via the mask. Kay feels at home behind the plaster visage, and suggests that to some extent we all do, because of its imposed safety. Kay, by the end of the book removes her mask, emerging as the metaphorical butterfly, who discovers that the love and approval she was searching for, has always been within.

Lauren Pope

Notes on Contributors

Fred D'Aguiar was born in London in 1960 but grew up in Guyana. He has published five poetry collections and four novels. His most recent works are *An English Sampler: Selected and New Poems* (Chatto) and the novel, *Bethany Bettany* (Chatto). He was Northern Arts Literary Fellow 1990–92 before moving to the US to teach creative writing and some literature classes. Currently he teaches in the English Dept at Virginia Tech in Virginia where he is Professor of English and Co-Director of the Masters of Fine Arts Program in Creative Writing.

Beatrice Fri Bime, a member of the British Council's Crossing Borders creative writing programme, hails from Cameroon, and has been writing since secondary school. Her work ranges from folklore, short stories and fiction to poetry. Published works include: *Mystique* and *Someplace, Somewhere*. Her poems 'Behind the Laughter', 'Flight Lt. James' and 'Posthumous' were published in Tide-Poles Peninsula College magazine, USA.

Jackee Budesta Batanda is a Ugandan writer, currently based in Johannesburg. She is studying for an MA in Forced Migration Studies at the University of the Witwatersrand. She has been Writer-in-Residence at Lancaster University and a fellow on British Council's Crossing Borders programme. Regional winner of the 2003 Commonwealth Short Story Competition, she has been highly commended for the Caine Prize for African Writing and short listed for the Macmillan Writers Prize for Africa. Her children's book, *The Blue Marble*, was published in conjunction with UNESCO-Paris and Sub-Saharan publishers (Ghana). Her short stories have been published in Uganda, England, USA, and Ghana and several have been broadcast on radio, including *Aciro's Song*.

Lizelle Bisschoff is a postgraduate student at the University of Stirling, researching the role of women in African cinema. She is the founder and director of 'Africa in Motion' (www. africa-in-motion.org.uk), an African film festival taking place at Filmhouse, Edinburgh, 20–29 October 2006.

Linda Cracknell is a freelance writer and creative writing teacher based in Highland Perthshire. In the late 1980s she was a VSO English teacher in Zanzibar and has returned to East Africa several times since, including in the role of mentor and workshop leader with Crossing Borders. Her first solo collection of short stories, *Life Drawing*, was published in 2000 and since then further work has been widely anthologised and appeared in journals. She also writes drama for BBC Radio.

Graham Fulton was born in 1959 and lives in Scotland. He has been writing and performing his poetry for the last twenty years. His poetry has been published in various magazines including *Ambit, The North, Edinburgh Review* and *Cencrastus*. His published collections include *Knights of the Lower Floors, Humouring the Iron Bar Man* (both Polygon), *This* (Rebel Inc.) and *Ritual Soup and other liquids* (Mariscat).

Gabriel Gidi is from Zimbabwe but he is currently living in Stoke on Trent, teaching and finishing a postgraduate degree. He was a participant in the Crossing Borders programme in 2004.

Martin Goodman was born in Leicester in 1956. He has worked in Germany, China, Saudi Arabia, Italy, the Netherlands, Thailand and Qatar; founded Scotland's premier video publishing business; toured as a professional actor; worked bars as an organist and pianist; and run a mobile music sales exhibition. A pilgrim to many of the sacred places around the globe, he has also walked through civil war zones of Eastern Turkey and Sri Lanka and visited remote refugee camps and relief projects. He teaches creative writing and has been shortlisted for the Whitbread Prize, awarded a Scottish Arts Council Writer's Bursary, Travel Awards from the Scottish Arts Council and the Society of Authors, a Royal Literary Fund Award, and an Authors Foundation Award. His journalism appears in *The Scotsman, The Financial Times, The Los Angeles Times*, etc.

Dorian Haarhoff is a South African poet and story-teller who facilitates creative writing workshops and acts as a writing mentor. He is a former Professor of English Literature at the University of Namibia. Since 1998 he has run his own business, Creative Workshops.

G.P. Kennedy is a writer and literary critic, with a host of impressive credits to his name. He is currently developing a novel, *Half Lived*, a satirical magazine, *The Standard*, and continues to work as reviews editor at online literary magazine *Incorporating Writing*. He recently moved to Liverpool where he shares a home with the loves of his life – family and books.

John Lindley is a poet and creative writing tutor. An experienced performer, he also runs poetry workshops for writers' groups, festivals and in prisons, schools, youth clubs and day care centres, as well as for those with mental and physical disabilities. Amongst his many other projects, he has been engaged on the British Council's Crossing Borders scheme, providing distance learning workshops for writers in Africa. His latest published collection of poetry is *Cheshire Rising*. He was appointed Cheshire Poet Laureate in 2004.

Jack Mapanje is Malawi's best known poet, linguist and human rights activist. Formerly head of department of English in the University of Malawi, he was imprisoned for about four years without trial or charge by Malawi's dictator Hastings Kamuzu Banda for his radical verse and dissenting views; he was released because of the campaign mounted by writers, linguists, journalists and human rights organisations and others globally. After three years as poet in residence at Dove Cottage, Grasmere, Cumbria, he joined the staff at the University of Newcastle where he teaches creative writing. He has published four books of poems, edited and co-edited four; his latest publication is *The Last of the Sweet Bananas: new and selected poems* (Bloodaxe Books). The poems published here are new and will appear in his next book of poems.

Graham Mort is an e-learning specialist and director of postgraduate studies in Creative Writing at Lancaster University. He designed and ran the African literature development programme Crossing Borders for the British Council from 2001–06. His latest book of poems is *A Night on the Lash* (Seren). He is currently working on *Visibility: New and Selected Poems* (Seren) and developing a new radio writing project in Uganda.

Beverley Naidoo was born in Johannesburg. As a student she joined the resistance to apartheid, leading to detention without trial and exile in England in 1965. Her award-winning fiction for young people includes *Journey to Jo'burg* (banned in South Africa until 1991), *Chain of Fire, No Turning Back, The Other Side of Truth* (Carnegie Medal 2000), *Web of Lies* and a short story collection *Out of Bounds* (Foreword by Archbishop Tutu). Plays include *The Playground* (*Time Out* Pick of the Year 2004). Her PhD explored teenagers' responses to literature and racism and she has honorary doctorates from the

University of Southampton and the Open University.

Meg Peacocke lives in rural Cumbria. Peterloo Poets have published three collections of her poetry, *Marginal Land, Selves* and *Speaking of the Dead*. In 2005 she received a Cholmondeley Award.

H.J. (Henning) Pieterse was born in 1960. He has published two volumes of poetry. *Alruin* (Mandrake) was awarded the Eugène Marais Prize, 1990, and the Ingrid Jonker Prize, 1991. *Die Burg van Hertog Bloubaard* (*Duke Bluebeard's Castle*) was awarded the Hertzog Prize in 2002, the highest accolade for Afrikaans writing. He has also published a volume of short stories, *Omdat Ons Alles Is* (*Because We Are Everything*). He is Associate Professor, Afrikaans and Dutch Linguistics, Poetry and Creative Writing, Department of Afrikaans and Theory of Literature, University of South Africa.

Christopher Mlalazi participated in Crossing Borders in 2004. He writes plays, fiction and poetry and is co-authoring a TV soap. He attended the 2005 Beyond Borders Literature Festival in Uganda and the 2006 Caine Prize Workshop. His stories have been published in five anthologies.

Wame Molefhe was born and raised in Francistown, Botswana. She now lives in Gaborone with her two children. She is the winner of the British Council (Botswana)/Alexander McCall Smith 2004 short story competition and recently completed a six-month writing mentorship programme, Crossing Borders, with the British Council. She has just completed a short creative writing programme with the University of South Africa.

Phillippa Yaa de Villiers was born in Hillbrow and grew up as a trans-racial adoptee in apartheid South Africa. What saved her sanity was writing and performing. She studied journalism at Rhodes University and later completed a two-year diploma in theatre at the Jacques Lecoq School of Theatre in Paris. She later completed an honours in Drama and Film, with screenwriting and physical theatre as her majors. She has written on a number of television series for South African television and one international collaboration with Swedish writer Charlotte Lesche. In 2005 she was a candidate on the Pansa/British Council's mentorship programme, Crossing Borders.

Hester Ross is from Islay and has lived in Shetland and Malawi where she taught in the English Literature Department at Chancellor College, Zomba. She currently lives in Leith and is a member of the MSc Creative Writing class at the University of Edinburgh. She is at work on a novel.

Kenneth R. Ross is Secretary of the Church of Scotland World Mission Council and an Honorary Fellow of the University of Edinburgh School of Divinity. From 1988 to 1998 he taught at Chancellor College, University of Malawi, where he became Professor of Theology. He has written and edited several books on Malawi, including *God, People and Power in Malawi* (CLAIM), *Gospel Ferment in Malawi* (Mambo Press), and *Democratization in Malawi: A Stocktaking* (CLAIM). He is Chair of the Board of the recently incorporated Scotland-Malawi Partnership.

Beth Webb worked for Crossing Borders for three years and visited Cameroon as part of the project. She has published poetry in several anthologies and nine children's books. Her first novel for teenagers, *Star Dancer*, is published in September 2006.